D. Niles

Please pray for her

CARMELITE
BECKLEY HILL
BARRE, VERMONT 05641

CARMELITE MONASTERY
BECKLEY HILL
BARRE, VERMONT 05641

Abbé Pierre

AND THE

RAGPICKERS OF EMMAUS

✶ ✶ ✶

Abbé Pierre

AND THE

RAGPICKERS OF EMMAUS

BY *Boris Simon*

TRANSLATED FROM THE FRENCH BY LUCIE NOEL

P. J. KENEDY & SONS

NEW YORK

ABBÉ PIERRE AND THE RAGPICKERS OF EMMAUS
is a translation of *Les Chiffoniers d'Emmaüs*
by Boris Simon (Paris, *Editions du Seuil,* 1954).

LIBRARY OF CONGRESS CATALOG CARD NUMBER: 55–5041
COPYRIGHT 1955 BY P. J. KENEDY & SONS, NEW YORK ©
PRINTED IN THE UNITED STATES OF AMERICA

Contents

I. A Light at the End of the Hard Road

II. The Ragpicker Builders

III. Hope Springs Eternal

LETTER FROM ABBÉ PIERRE
TO THE AUTHOR

My dear Boris:

You wanted to tell the story of Emmaus, and to do so with greater understanding, you came several times to live among us here. You tackled this difficult subject with all your heart, truthfully, yet with the necessary discretion that certain cases imposed.

Let us hope no one will misinterpret your message. Your book is not so much a story of what my comrades and I have done; rather, it is the tale of what happened to us. For we are all deeply conscious of the fact that in this wonderful, hard, and tragic story we were led. We know quite well that we are the same as we were, no better than before. We were simply privileged to have been thrown into the very heart of things. It was as though a hurricane had hurled us into human suffering, the source of true life. In the face of this, men unite for survival. One saves oneself in saving others.

May fresh dedication spring from your book. May it awaken consciences and inspire men with the will to act.

One day a child of ten wrote me:

"We were so miserable when we had no roof over our heads. . . . I thought all men were cruel. Now I think perhaps I was wrong. Maybe there are more good people than bad. Only then I had never met them. . . ."

May your book hasten the day when no child in this world will be tempted to believe in the cruelty of men.

May God bless you and yours.

H.-A. GROUÈS-PIERRE
Emmaus, Christmas '53
Neuilly-Plaisance (Seine-et-Oise)

AUTHOR'S FOREWORD

THE first French edition of this book was on the presses when an event took place which made a profound impression on public opinion in France and throughout the world. During the night of January 3, 1954, the Council of the French Government had just rejected a bill demanding funds to build emergency housing for the poor when a three-month-old baby died of cold in the abandoned shell of a public bus in Paris. This drama would have passed unnoticed had Abbé Pierre not written to the Minister of Reconstruction an indignant letter in which he invited the Minister to attend the baby's funeral. Thereupon followed events which have no precedent in the annals of the French Republic. The Minister attended the funeral, and, following the baby's coffin on foot, decided then and there that the French Government should intervene in this grievous situation. Funds for the building of several Emergency Cities were decided upon at the next session of the Council.

Three weeks later, in February, crossing Paris on an icy cold night, Abbé Pierre saw groups of men sleeping outdoors. He saw them lying on the sidewalks over subway vents, trying to keep warm. They were huddled in doorways and under bridges. This everyday, yet nonetheless intolerable, sight was all the more shocking with the temperature at ten degrees below zero. Helped by the ragpickers, he bought and pitched a tent on an empty lot in the heart of one of the oldest sections of Paris.

On the air he launched a pathetic appeal:

"My friends, come to the rescue. Every night men and women are

3

dying of cold in the streets of Paris. Last night we found a woman who had died of exposure holding her eviction papers in her hand. Such disgraces must stop. Help me to fight the horrible and the ridiculous."

This appeal was answered by Paris and all of France. One of the better hotels in the Champs-Elysées district offered Abbé Pierre office space and storerooms. The police had the warm subways, police stations, and railroad terminals opened after hours to the poor and the destitute. Public foundations and private hostels sheltered some 10,000 homeless tramps, young workmen, and married couples with children. Tons of clothing and blankets poured in along with hundreds of millions of francs.

Abbé Pierre called this the "Insurrection of Kindness." It was the expression of an entire nation whose generosity was awakened by the voice of a modern St. Vincent de Paul. And this was no sudden impulse without a future. At the gates of Paris entire villages are rising up to shelter the disinherited have-nots of the nation. France has taken the question of her poor in hand.

PREFACE

You yourselves told us this story, Companions of Emmaus, standing in wind-swept fields on bitter winter days, or crouching beneath a storm lamp in an abandoned railroad car bogged down in the mud of a building lot. We have tried to relate your intense, gripping experiences, to tell how you and your families huddled together under a tent, or in a gypsy wagon, waiting for the hour when you could move into the house you and your companions were building. However, in quoting facts, anecdotes, and words, we were obliged out of consideration for personal lives to leave many things unsaid. This, we might say, was our most delicate task: to remain within the bounds of truth, yet not give away the identity of those who preferred to remain unknown. There were other cases where, on the contrary, we described a personality exactly as we saw it or made one composite of a thousand cases, drawing from a passing event a profound meaning to make plausible what people have called the "miracle" of Emmaus.

Have we been able to retain the essential? We hope so. In any case, such as it is, here is your book—neither a novel nor a literary essay. But may it help others know something of this experience, which by its proof of human fraternity, its spiritual riches and social significance, has already aroused the interest of the entire world. It is a story of tears, of blood, and of courage. It is also the story of the faith of one man and a group of men at grips with the shame and misery brought on by war, by alcohol, by lack of shelter, and by all social injustices. (In telling this story, an author wary of writing in bad

5

taste might be reluctant to introduce melodrama. But life itself, and particularly the life of poor people, has a veritable genius for being melodramatic.)

Why is it that Emmaus holds such interest and fascination in the hearts of so many French people and foreigners? First, because of its role as a haven for lonely men and desperate men, for those hit by misfortune and by the very "mechanics" (born through circumstances) of its rescues. In Paris as well as in the suburbs there are many other charity organizations: homes, shelters, hostels, centers, and institutions where distress cases by the thousands are given bed and board. Among these is the Nanterre Home, literally a small town, where some 5,000 poor are cared for. But this exterior and temporary aid does not always get at the deep inner life of the recipient. Only too few and far between are the religious and lay organizations where human dignity and a true reason for living can be restored.

This is what Emmaus offers. The poor of Emmaus help one another, forming a free and equal community of workers. This is one of its greatest secrets. Together they work, toil, hope, risk, and together they save one another. They owe nothing to anyone. Here they are helping themselves; they feel less like victims of charity. The ex-deputy goes ragpicking at the side of the ex-convict. Distinctions between race, creed, and political beliefs disappear the moment one enters this unique community.

And the Companion of Emmaus sees direct results and benefits from his hard labor as ragpicker. His profit makes it possible for another lost soul to come to Emmaus, for an ex-convict to find shelter. Nothing is achieved except through his heart. So the man who was a derelict becomes a savior. This key thought is illustrated in the story of the tramp Djibouti.

It was not merely because he was welcomed to the center that this tough man experienced a feeling of gratitude. In addition he was given the possibility of restoring his self-respect, through his work, through his own acts of kindness to those still more unfortunate than he. Nothing in this world helps a man more to regain his self-confidence than to feel he is wanted and needed by someone.

The second and most important reason for the existence of Emmaus? It shelters the homeless. Today, at long last, the scandal of the lack of housing for the poor of France has exploded in broad daylight. But for many years it was a secret disgrace. Poorly informed public opinion dozed pleasantly while the public powers toyed in a leisurely way with grandiose projects.

Experts labor over plans. City planners, legislators, and administrators have great vision, but they work on paper. They are unaware of the fact that this very evening shelter may be a life-and-death matter for a family wandering in the rain with a child dying of cold. Too often the greatest source of action to achieve social improvements is tears. Tears of mourning, tears of shame, tears of indignation and despair.

The founder of Emmaus and his Companions had suffered themselves, had seen these tears of the have-nots, of the young families struggling to exist, living and dying outdoors. They went forward to meet this army of distressed people, taking charge of them spontaneously, without so much as a vestige of a plan. They found their strength in their will to act.

"Welcome them first, help them next." And in every instance the solution, whether human or providential, did occur. This daring, this sacred flame, is similar to that which inspired St. Vincent de Paul. For only men of great faith could immerse themselves in the depression, the horror of certain situations without losing heart. Confident in the support of the Almighty, only they could derive sources of strength, of life—even of joy—from these experiences.

They started from nothing, with no preconceived plan, answering the call day by day, aiding the most urgent cases. From there the movement has developed into something more than just a provisional solution to the tragic housing problem that affects the poor and downtrodden have-nots of Paris. It has developed into a city, a city of resurrected souls, where each person finds himself by helping his neighbor; and in finding himself he is once more prepared to go out into the world to live a normal and decent life. The creation of the first Emergency Cities for the poor in Paris will surely give impetus to similar projects in other parts of France. Initiative, awakened by this example of fervent generosity, will spring up. Because the legislators themselves have finally realized that this is a national problem, and its solution a national duty, this initiative will stand an excellent chance of being put into concrete shape and substance.

In telling the history of a movement linked to life itself, the story can end only when the events of time are unfurled and spent. For that reason this book remains unfinished. The sap animating Emmaus surges up with such force that the bark of the tree cracks. In but a few months the scene has changed. We have written the first act of the drama, when the jobless and homeless were welcomed only with hope; when the ground was broken for these Emergency Cities before any funds were in hand for the work that was to be done; when in a moment of deep distress the priest went out on the streets to beg. Then followed more problems and the solution with "organized begging," when the Emmaus beggars tangled with the Paris beggars, and when, finally, they organized their veritable junkyard at Emmaus. It was a question of all or nothing at all, and eventually "all" was achieved.

The unrolling of these events illustrates the unforeseen and indisputable fact that, in this great undertaking, something intervened which went beyond individual man and even human conception.

In introducing and bringing onto the stage the creator of Emmaus, we had to overcome his scruples. It was impossible to omit the personal role of Abbé Pierre without undermining the structure of the story. We have endeavored to present his deeds with the greatest fidelity, as well as to quote verbatim as many of his sayings as possible.

This book will have reached its goal if it succeeds in making the reader aware of two things: the misery of millions of poor human beings living in the midst of civilized people—a scandal of our twentieth century—and the courage of a few who have shared this misery in order to combat and destroy it.

1953

B. S.

✶ I ✶

A LIGHT AT THE END
OF THE HARD ROAD

1: *Djibouti the Tramp*

THIS particular night of November 1950 was bitterly cold. Djibouti knew he would come down with pneumonia if he slept again on sacks and old newspapers in the ramshackle woodshed in the alley. It was as damp as a well. It stank of garbage and urine, wedged as it was between the St. Paul district tenements which had been declared unsanitary.

At 4 A.M., shivering with cold, he made his way to Les Halles, the Paris night market. Here he was hired by a wholesale cheese merchant as an extra hand to unload the rush baskets filled with Brie cheese. He worked for an hour, and the boss gave him a 100-franc note and a cheese. Silently Djibouti walked away.

"Might at least say 'thank you,' " growled the man.

But in cases like that Djibouti never said "thank you." He had worked. He had been paid. He was even with all, and no one need be thanked. This way he remained free. Liberty and justice were two words Djibouti silently repeated from time to time, just to give himself courage to go a little further. He mixed very little with the world of tramps, beggars, and vermin-covered drunkards that his social standing brought across his horizon in such places as the Bread Crumb (a French charitable canteen), the Salvation Army canteen, and the Red Cross hostel. They called him Deaf-and-Dumb, the Bear, or the Philosopher.

His philosophy, such as it was, limited itself to several bitter conclusions that he kept to himself. They went rather like this: "At forty-eight you don't reshape your destiny, even if under your beggar's trappings you retain some vestige of personal dignity." (In the soldier's kitbag which Djibouti always carried was a toothbrush, a cake of soap, and a sewing kit.) "Even if you keep clean, give yourself an almost-daily shave, even if you never get drunk, you remain forever outside real life, beyond all hope, because no one really cares. It's best to make up your mind early to the futility of it all, to rid yourself of the luxury of hope. When you're all alone, by yourself, that's not very good company. Keeps body and soul together, that's all. Sink down into life, backward as it were, and shut your eyes tight so you won't remember too much about it. The great secret is to be able to kill all desire in yourself. What's left? A bitter sense of liberty. But liberty—what is it? Unless you can share it with someone, offer it up as gift to someone you love, it doesn't mean much. And when there is no one left to love? . . ."

There remained, too, Djibouti's unrootable obsession of universal justice. He thought about this, but decided it was the dream of a lunatic—something one enjoyed but was never fooled by.

Djibouti was not a tramp by vocation. He was a worn man who looked ten years older than he was. A scar seared across the side of his face, running from his left jaw to his right temple and catching his nose. Strong, slow, and wild-looking, he rarely smiled. The deep scar accentuated his troubled, hostile look. No, by no means was Djibouti good-looking. But his blue eyes had a serious, anxious expression, and a kind of candid timidity which inspired a feeling of confidence.

The scar: a souvenir of Africa. From 1930 to 1935 he had been a truck driver for a Franco-Ethiopian transport company, running from Djibouti to Addis Ababa—hence his nickname. A few days after the Italians occupied the Ethiopian capital he was a chance witness to a horrible scene. Two drunken sergeants had tied a native to a pole and were scorching his naked body with an acetylene torch. Blind with rage, Djibouti intervened, got into a melee, and was slashed across the face with a dagger.

Back in Paris he purchased a truck of his own and hired out to various contractors. Then he married and started to build a house at Villeneuve-St. Georges. He lived in his little house only two months. War came, his truck was requisitioned, and he was drafted to Alsace.

Two years later, in the prison where he was sent by the Germans, a letter from his wife informed him that their house had been demolished during an American bombing. She asked him for power of attorney to sell what she had salvaged. That was the last letter she ever wrote him. On the train, coming home, Djibouti said to himself, "All is not lost." He was only forty-three years old. He had the courage to start from scratch, to find his wife, to forgive her. With the price he could get for his property he could buy himself another truck and begin all over again.

He never found his wife. Neighbors told him that Germans had lived in the house, that a child had been born in '43. As for what was left of the house and garden, she had liquidated everything before disappearing. All Djibouti had left was his mustering-out pay. Maybe sometime later he would get compensation from the government for the years he was a prisoner.

He hired out as driver to a public utilities company. For a month he drove a fifteen-ton fully-loaded truck from Paris to Orléans.

Djibouti told us his story practically all in one breath, and we have written it as he told it. But how can one tell whether his wife's departure, the ruin of his happiness, did not haunt him by night on the road? Or whether, as he drove his truck, his hands did not clench the wheel in agony? He never drank. However, in a driving rain near Étampes one night he ran into a car, killing a woman and a little girl. He himself was dragged out of the truck with a broken leg. The court acquitted him of manslaughter, citing foul weather and the bad highway as extenuating circumstances. But these things by no means explained all in the accident. During the two months he spent in the hospital he tried to understand how he could have, for the space of three seconds, lost control—a fit of faintness, an instant's loss of consciousness? The doctor who examined him growled: "Possibly you were sober, but your father—wasn't he an alcoholic?"

Unable to drive again, Djibouti worked as a mechanic in a garage for two years. After his accident, besides developing a slight limp, his face would occasionally be rippled by a jumping nerve. His hands, too, would suddenly start trembling, and this he could not control. His boss suspected him of drinking. But Djibouti was always sober and smoked hardly at all. His hands, though, daily became more awkward. Afraid of being fired, he took the initiative himself, and got a job as a packer in a department store. Next he tried his luck as a service-station attendant, and finally as a workman in a junk lot. But despite his efforts, he could not do the work required on any job. The nauseating depression which had started when he left the hospital was slowly getting the better of him. The struggle to make ends meet, merely to exist, expressed itself in an overwhelming fatigue. Look for another job. Start new rounds in search of work. What for? He felt more and more remote from reality, an outsider, an alien.

One day he returned to his hotel to find his few possessions on the landing and the door to his room locked. The hotel manager was unwilling to rent by the month. He would now rent only by the night. Djibouti then realized that the best thing to do would be to reconcile himself to the parasite-like existence of a public ward. He placed his name on the unemployment list, went on relief, and during the summer was able to lay aside a little money for the coming winter. He slept in free public and private hostels in town, and, more often than not, under the stars in the country.

He began then to know the desolate peace of long, solitary walks, his kitbag slung over his shoulder. He stocked it with oats, tea, and half-decayed fruit and vegetables, collected off the floors of food markets. Once a week he had a bowl of soup at the Bread Crumb or the Salvation Army canteen.

During the summer the suburbs of Paris offer homeless derelicts more shelter than the city. But those who know the ups and downs of this sort of life know that most of this population of tramps, ragpickers, and beggars must also camp in these suburbs under starkly primitive conditions during the winter months. Near Aubervilliers, a factory suburb outside of Paris, this type of camper runs into several thousands. They settle in what is left of a building shack (if they're lucky enough to find one vacant), in the hollows formed by empty quarries at Romainville, on the banks along St. Martin's Canal, under the plane trees of the island of La Jatte, in the pillboxes opposite Place Victor—two steps from the French Air Ministry. Tribes of Arabs live in huts made of old sacks and string, families of ragpickers live in rabbit hutches, professional gypsies live in wagons with broken wheels, solitary vagabonds find shelter beneath scraggly bushes, where they cook their evening meals in pots balanced on three stones.

In summer, Djibouti haunted the suburb quays, solitary and taciturn, avoiding all contact with these have-nots. In winter, he would return to the center of Paris and painfully install himself in some hidden shelter. In quest of a free bed he would prowl around the backs of prosperous Rue St. Honoré stores, searching along their corridors, dark and reeking like sewer drains, filled with baskets, wooden crates, stacks of paper, and alive with rats. One afternoon he discovered the attic of an old house in the Rue de la Huchette, an airless place with no light. He installed himself there but almost suffocated and left in haste the next day at dawn. And there was the room in the Passage de l'Avenir, with no windows and no light, where he was dragged by a chance acquaintance one evening. The man was one of a group of about twenty others who rented this hovel. They were street singers, ragpickers, jobless artists, hucksters. There they slept, on newspapers, huddled close to each other to keep warm. In the subway, of course, he could always get a few hours of warmth and sleep, but he lived in fear of being taken in for vagrancy by the police.

In February of 1949 he was caught stealing fish in Les Halles and spent a month in jail. After, he made his way to the Nanterre Home for the poor, taking his place among 5,000 other homeless wanderers receiving free food and shelter. Here he found a kind of halfway security in idleness and met Sebastien, a crackpot professor, who kept repeating half to himself, "Life—this can't be it; it just can't be like this—to end up this way. Real life must be somewhere else, otherwise, so help us, we've been betrayed." The others would shrug their shoulders. Only Djibouti understood and shared his anguish and despair, for this was the voice of Djibouti himself, a voice echoing his own dream of a world filled with liberty and justice for everyone . . . a better end than the Nanterre Home.

When he left the Home in May, Djibouti took with him this thought: "True life is elsewhere, perhaps nearer than we think: perhaps within ourselves." For he had known real life, with his love, his wife, before the war. Real life was love, but that seemed to be irretrievably buried in the past. Had he been an intellectual, maybe Djibouti would have ended it all. But he lacked the imagination necessary to dramatize life. Dragging his game leg day after day, urged on by a few natural instincts, he would wander from place to place, seemingly finding enough to occupy his mind. For two whole years he walked, stopped, slept, looked, ate, did little, said little, rarely said "thank you"— because he never asked for anything—and nevertheless enjoyed confusedly his liberty. But two things distinguished him from the other derelicts dragging their soles across the city. First, his cleanliness. His soap-filled kitbag was his only valuable possession. Second, despite his misery, Djibouti never drank, and was always lucid.

So, while drinking his black coffee at the counter of a cheap bistro this November morning after unloading cheese at Les Halles, Djibouti thought back on his life, and he ached body and soul. His tired limbs cried out for a good night's sleep in a real bed. He decided then and there to start his "rounds of the priests." It was distasteful to him, this idea of begging, but how tired he was, how he hoped for a meal or a bed—or even a note of recommendation to a charity home. That very day he would pull the bell at the gates of a priory sometime around dusk. Then the soup would be ready and the priest would not have the heart to send him away into the icy night.

The first doorbell he rang that evening was answered by a young priest. Having listened to Djibouti's story, he told him he could not give him shelter, but picked up the telephone. Then:

"You will go to Emmaus," he said. "Here is the address, and take this for the subway and the bus."

Djibouti was tempted for a moment to spend the 100-franc note on a bowl of soup. After all, he could always scrounge around for a place to sleep. It was the proximity of the subway station that proved the decisive factor, made him change his mind and decide to give this other "Home" a try.

It was an hour later and night had fallen when Djibouti reached the address the priest had given him. It was in an eastern suburb, a large house set in an even larger yard, and the gate to the yard was open. However, there seemed to be no sign of life. There was light back of a red curtain on the second floor and on the street level, to the left, rays of light filtered fanwise through the mist. Djibouti leaned on the railings to get his breath. The climb had been tough, and his poorly mended leg ached.

A wooden panel on the gate read: Emmaus, Home of Social Action and International Relations.

These words told the story of the Home, a story known now by millions, but then only three years old. And in the future, Djibouti was to play a large part in this story.

2: *The Family under the Tarpaulin*

LEANING against the high wall of the Citroën automobile factory, tiny Madame Vatier, a few months pregnant, stood talking to her husband. Close by, their eighteen-month-old baby slept in her carriage.

"He told me he needed the room tonight," her husband was saying. Clenching his fists, he said to himself, "Here we go again."

Then, without too much conviction, he added, "After all, it was to be expected."

"I agree, Marcel, but he had no right to throw me out. I only went out for five minutes to get Noëlle some milk, and when I got back our things were in the hall and the baby was crying in her carriage. The door to the room was locked."

"The dog—I hope at least you didn't pay him."

"I had to. He had my coat and would have kept it."

The October dusk was falling and there was a light, penetrating mist.

"Come on, Germaine. We'll find something in the Rue du Commerce. I have my pay. It will all work out."

He gave his young wife a kiss and leaned over the baby.

"Eh, angel, it will all work out, won't it?"

So they spent four days in a hotel on the Rue du Commerce. Then the proprietor told them that their neighbor, a salesman, had complained of the baby crying at night. He "needed the room."

They tried a tiny hotel on the Rue de la Convention, but on seeing the baby buggy the proprietor's wife made a face.

"For three of you?"

She sighed and, lowering her voice, said:

"Look, I understand, believe me. But my husband says he won't have married couples with children. But maybe for one night only—I'll give you a room at 600 francs."

That night they slept in a bed. Next morning, before going to work, Marcel took their large suitcase and left it in the care of a café. His wife walked the streets all day pushing the baby carriage. Toward evening rain started to fall.

Again she went to wait for him at the plant.

"Listen," she said, a tinge of hesitation in her voice. "A woman told me today about an institution where I could go with the baby."

"What about me? Must we be separated?"

"No, I'm just going for the baby—just for a few days."

"O.K., then, I'll go to the Salvation Army center."

Marcel was ashamed. He was a workman, neither a tramp nor a derelict. He disliked welfare centers and hostels. He disliked accepting charity. He only saw his family in the evening, during the night, and now even at night he had to be separated from them. But it had to be faced because it was not even the middle of the month and more than half of his pay was gone.

So for the next three days they met for only a few hours every evening, sitting in a bistro. And they had to leave each other too quickly, because the Salvation Army closed its doors early.

On the third day Germaine said: "I'm not going back to the Foundation any more."

"Why not?"

"The directress told me I should place the child in the Home."

"At the Public Welfare Home? Never."

"But Marcel, she said I could always claim her back when I wanted to. That she would be well cared for—that . . ."

"No," the man said. "No. No."

The problem was as simple as that. Find a room and lose the child or stay on the streets together. They chose the streets.

First they rang the doorbell of a priest who recommended a home run by nuns. There wasn't a single vacancy. They were sent on to another home. Finally they ended up by sleeping on the quay by the river.

Sunday was fine. The sun was warm, almost like springtime. They spent the day sitting on a grass mound in an empty lot near the Porte de Versailles. Planes passed by flying low to the Issy-les-Moulineaux landing field. They could see nearby, huge, half-finished apartment buildings, their white façades shining brightly in contrast to the dark honeycomb of unfinished windows. The man said to himself that when these buildings were finished they would have no right to an apartment there either. Rents would be too high.

And all over Paris other thousands of empty cells, tens of thousands of empty rooms might have sheltered them that night —a room, a room, a room! But again they would have no room to sleep in.

Late in the afternoon they gathered their few possessions and walked on. All they had left until the end of the month was 4,000 francs. They had to watch their step. But the night would be mild.

Finally, Marcel discovered a fence at the foot of the railroad embankment near the Place Balard. They could sleep outdoors, behind the fence, under a bush. There they would be together. They would lie on the ground, wearing their coats, covered by the blanket. The child would rest in her carriage. But they would be together, after all these long nights of separation.

The idea of spending the night under the stars somewhat scared the girl. Suppose the baby cried or caught cold? What if the gendarmes caught them and gave them a warning? But Marcel, on the contrary, was amused by the idea. It reminded him of the times he had gone camping with his friends from the Youth Hostels, ten years back.

"We'll tell the cops we're on a picnic. We're free, aren't we?"

And then suddenly: "Forgive me, Germaine. I'm thoughtless; the ground will be too hard for you."

"No, don't worry about me," she said; "that's nonsense."

So they had their supper on the embankment and the baby slept peacefully in her carriage.

That night Marcel took his wife in his arms and talked to her quietly of a favorite idea he had had for spending fifteen days of "paid vacation" in Bourganeuf, at Mother Vatier's—whom Germaine had not yet met.

"You'll see what a wonderful woman she is. A real old-fashioned mother. She lives in a tiny house with a bit of garden, a little enclosure, complete with a goat. When I was a kid . . ."

Two years ago, just after they were married, Marcel wrote his mother that they had found a small furnished apartment, which was the truth at the time. He had sublet one from his friend Claude. The boy got married himself six months later and wanted his apartment, so Marcel and Germaine took a room in a hotel. But in order not to upset Mother Vatier's peace of mind, they still sent her Claude's address as their own. And never had Marcel so much as breathed a word to her of all their trials and tribulations, of moving from room to room—first from a furnished apartment to a friend's room, then on to hotel rooms which brought his meager pay check to an end all too soon. Always this agonizing struggle for nightly shelter, even worse since the baby's birth, a never ending march from one place to another. And the knowledge that thousands of others were going in this same infernal circle, that this inhuman condition was now almost routine existence for the common laborer, was hardly of much comfort.

And how could poor old Mother Vatier, tucked away in her tiny house at Bourganeuf, ever be expected to understand all this? Why upset her, make her sick with anxiety? Every year they planned to spend their vacation with her, but somehow they never could find the courage to face her inevitable questions.

"This year it's a cinch—we'll go."

Germaine allowed herself to be persuaded to dream, along with her husband, lying there on the railroad slope under the stars.

About midnight a train rolled slowly by, barely a few yards from where they lay. Then they dozed.

But not for long. A stray dog started barking on the other side of the fence. Marcel got up and threw a pebble at him. Now the baby, awakened by the noise, would not stop crying. She was hungry. But how could they heat her bottle? How could one make a fire without attracting attention?

Then the mother took the child in her arms and for the first time broke into a fit of weeping. The tears took Marcel by surprise, for generally she was so courageous and confident. He timidly touched her shoulder, but she pushed him away.

"I'm leaving. I'm leaving tomorrow for Abbeville. I can't take it any longer."

He said nothing, and lit a cigarette. Maybe she was right. Maybe it would be best for her to go home to her parents. They were a bourgeois family, and, even though she didn't get on with them too well (mainly because of her marriage to him), at least there she and the child would have a roof over their heads. And the next one could have a decent birth.

"O.K. You do as you think best, Germaine."

Then she called to him. "Marcel, come here."

Putting her free arm around him, she wept on his shoulder. With this a sudden rage enveloped him. It gave him an idea, lots of ideas. Tomorrow he would not go to work. He would go to the City Hall and demand a roof for himself and his family. "It's up to them to find us a room." He would go and raise Cain at the Prefecture of Police. He would go to the editor of *Humanité* so that they could write about his case. He would go to the priests. To anyone. He would go to all the city offices he knew. He hated and feared them but he was fed up. He must get a room come what may—a room where they would not be thrown out three days later and a room that would not cost two thirds of a day's earnings.

Germaine did not leave for Abbeville. Leaving him would have been cowardly.

So Marcel went to the City Hall. They took his name. They told him they would put him on a priority list. They would check his identity and let him know. In this way he found out that in Paris alone there were 64,000 applications for 900 low-rent apartments.

That afternoon he returned to the plant. There, as he poured out his story to his friend Claude, the latter offered to sell him a heavy canvas cover.

"You can pitch it in an empty lot, just like a tent. At least you'll have your own corner. Spread straw on the ground, close it tight around you; you won't feel the cold. It's the way the Arabs camp out at Aubervilliers and they seem comfortable enough."

"But Germaine is pregnant, and my kid isn't even two years old . . ." He hesitated, and then bought the cover.

"Listen," said his friend. "I can show you a place where you can live in peace. It's not far from the factory. Not over twenty minutes' ride on a bike."

The deserted lot, disfigured by heaps of chalk and creviced by mudholes and a deserted quarry, was dotted with scattered hawthorn bushes and an occasional small tree.

In the distance, beyond the kitchen gardens belonging to the vegetable growers, they could see a few villas and several low-rent apartment houses under construction.

Surveying this scene, Germaine said, "I don't want to see anyone, and I don't want anyone to see me."

On the main highway, not over 400 yards away, they could hear the roar of passing cars. But from the tent all they could see were bushes on the slopes of the chalk pits and a small tree growing on the edge of one of the pits, silhouetted against the sky—and as solitary in appearance as if it had been growing on top of a sand dune at the end of the world.

There they lived for thirteen months. Germaine cooked their meals on a tiny stove which Marcel had bought at the Flea Market. A storm lamp gave them light, and they slept on straw. They carried their water and supplies from the crossroads. The tent was so low they could not stand upright. The November rains transformed their chalky yard into a milklike swamp.

Then one day Marcel wrote: "Dear Mother, now we have our own little home, still very humble, only one room. Soon we hope to enlarge it . . ." And suddenly he stopped writing. "Why can't I build my own house?"

The thought became an obsession. To build their own house. A neat home all their own, where no one would have the right to put them out, where his children would have the security of a roof over their heads.

He talked to a few friends first.

"You believe in Santa Claus? If you think that a worker, on his own, with his pay, can build a house . . . Before you lay the first brick, you need, besides the price of the land, about 100,000 francs besides for getting in water lines, lights, the sewer systems, and all that."

"Then I must die in my tent and not ever live in a house?"

Marcel, however, the title carried no significance whatsoever—it meant even less than his status of priest.

"We know what they're all worth." Marcel shrugged.

"But," Germaine said, "you should have seen the look in his eyes. Then you would trust him the way I do."

A priest just like the others. And his Home of Emmaus, it must be just the same as the others: a bed for three days, and then outside to die.

3: *The House That Was too Big Youth Hostel*

S EVERAL years before these events, on an October morning in 1947, a car bearing the tricolor cockade of a Parliament member drew up to a deserted house.

"But it's in ruins," murmured the priest as he stepped from the car. He was accompanied by a white-haired lady.

"The agent really promised us nothing else," was her reply.

A fallen tree had broken through the rusty fence. Brambles and nettles invaded the court. Through its sightless eyes the poor building contemplated the visitors with such a pitiful expression that the priest was almost tempted to smile.

Once this house had been a handsome bourgeois residence. Just as he was always drawn to human misery, there was something about the misfortune of the former dwelling that attracted him. It seemed truly as if the house were silently pleading for them to drag it out of its abandonment, from this slow decay of deserted things. It cried for a life, a destiny, a soul. In days past it had undoubtedly been a comfortable home, a place that rang with laughter, a meeting place for family, for friends, or even lovers. In the park children had once played by the pool. Young girls had swung on the rope swing beneath the acacias. On warm Sundays fine ladies wearing their Sunday best had taken tea on the lawn. Gentlemen had smoked a last cigar in the garden before having a game of billiards in the large pavilion at the left of the yard. The remnants of this period, the marble chimneypiece, the once-rich draperies and wallpaper, suggested a refined way of life. Certainly the house could never have dreamed the part it was destined soon to play, or what service would be demanded from it by this gray-haired spinster and the small priest who now on this October morning were having such trouble forcing open the gate. How could the house dream that the respectable bourgeois family would be followed by a community of ragpickers?

The visitors, picking their way over empty cans, rags, and all kinds of garbage, advanced through the yard and onto the porch —also covered with litter—and passed under the columns which supported the second-floor balcony. The ground floor, because of its barracklike appearance, recalled the successive phases of soldiers who had been billeted there. Germans, Americans, members of the Resistance. Empty cans, mildewed blankets, piles of planks, and stacks of papers. In the ceiling gaped a huge hole from which water dripped.

Gingerly climbing up an insecure staircase, the visitors ventured onto the second floor. Here fungous growths covered the wall plaster and the paper hung in strips. Water was oozing through the roof. Decay had set in, and the beams and paneling were falling apart. The bathroom, with its bathtub retrieved from the cellar, had itself become a bathtub, the water reaching several inches up the walls.

Finally they made their way to the park, now more a jungle of neglect: under the great golden boughs, through the undergrowth of brambles, nettles, and thistles, more empty cans caught the rays of a pale sun. In spots, the ground was mottled with sunlight and carpeted with dead leaves that overflowed onto the shimmering surface of a pool. The sun, too, was pleading in its own way for this pitiful paradise.

What prompted the future tenants to make their final decision may have been the sight of two splendid apple trees, laden with their last magnificent fruit. It seemed as if they had been waiting for this visit before letting the apples fall to the ground. And the visitors accepted the property's humble homage. That very evening the lease was signed.

The first appearance of the new proprietor of this hopeless abode in no way disappointed the curiosity of the neighbors. On a lovely afternoon in the Indian summer they spied him perched on the roof of the house, a small, thin man with a black beard, casual in his shirt sleeves and khaki pants. He clung with one hand to the gable and with the other he scooped off the layer of dead leaves. A man—and a very different man indeed from the traditional image of a priest or deputy.

From that day on the sound of the hammer announced the "Beaver's" presence. Back from Paris, he would cast off his priest's garb and the worries of the Chamber of Deputies to be just a man rebuilding his house.

And it all started, said Abbé Pierre, because the house was too big.

A small office room and a corner where he could sleep were all he needed. At that moment Abbé Pierre did not foresee that, by its very size, this house would serve to alleviate the distress of the homeless in the neighborhood. His only thought on the first day was to be able to share the place with the family of a friend, a member of the upper house of Parliament in quest of an apartment. He would let him have the ground floor. As for the park and the annexes—what a wonderful opportunity they presented for workers' meetings, for the scouts who are always looking around the suburbs for some place to hold their weekly troop reunions. But all this waste space, these empty rooms—when such multitudes were in need of a roof over their heads so they could live like human beings!

First of all, though, to make the house livable.

After long sessions of the Chamber of Deputies, the Father would go around to visit contractors, house painters, and carpenters. He bought planks and tools by the hundreds. Soon the very walls of the old house shook with hammering that brought out even the mice. Mademoiselle, his white-haired secretary, helped him arrange the interior. On the floor, under the rafters, he set up partitions and fixed six small rooms, so that workmen's families could come there to spend quiet week-ends. Filled with the enthusiasm of the builder, a typical trait in Abbé Pierre's character that was later to be amply revealed, he proposed to install a mess hall, a kitchen, to build bungalows and a chapel. For furniture he made the rounds of the Flea Market, of secondhand dealers and of peddlers, buying up tables, chairs, folding beds,

stoves. Strapped to the luggage rack of his Citroën, decorated
with the deputy's tricolor cockade, he carried these treasures back
to the house.

Thus, for a period of about two years this house knew a peaceful existence, with the member of the upper house of Parliament
on the ground floor and Abbé Pierre upstairs on the second floor.

From Saturday to Monday various groups took over the park.
Absorbed by his parliamentary duties, the priest gave them full
run of the place. Young families celebrating a christening, choral
societies rehearsing their program, seminary students or deputies
getting a breath of fresh air, groups of workmen intent on discussing social problems, youths from Charenton or Montreuil
pitching their tents in the park—these were his guests.

The kitchen garden bore vegetables and fruit, the yard was
filled with lilies and rosebushes. Nothing yet pointed to the up-
heaval which was soon to transform the estate's peaceful existence.

Watching these weekly pilgrims turn to this place of comfort
away from the city, the priest recalled the village to which two
disciples of Jesus, broken by the great calamity of the crucifixion,
had departed from Jerusalem. In the humble inn at Emmaus
they had passed through despair and encountered hope. The
same might happen here in his house. For this place in the
suburbs might mean just that—a meeting place of peace and
joy.

In giving his house the symbolic name of Emmaus, the priest
thought only of the spiritual uplift and the temporary comfort a
visit here might mean to certain ones. But soon the house was
actually to rescue lives in mortal danger. Just as thousands of
other desperate and homeless persons, Djibouti, jobless and discouraged, wandered about Paris, sick to death of hoping, and
sick, too, with despair. Just as thousands of others, the Vatier
family had settled down under their tarpaulin on a pallet of
mud and straw.

This hearth in Abbé Pierre's house had as yet not known the
baptism of tears. But here in the spring of '49 came the first
permanent guest. A man of about forty, with snow-white hair,
mild yet taciturn, Bastien, an ex-convict, was the first in misery

to be adopted. The movements of his hands were awkward for, beneath the bandages, his wrists still bore the scars of his recent attempt on his own life.

By summer the house, which had been placed on the lists of the Central Office of Youth Hostels, was preparing to welcome its young visitors who were to converge on Paris from other parts of France, from Europe, and all over the world.

As president of the executive committee of the universal movement for World Federation, Abbé Pierre wished to give the adherents of this movement the possibility of an inexpensive visit to Paris. He purchased, on the installment plan, the empty huts of the prisoners' camps at Saint-Denis, had them brought to Emmaus, and, with the aid of Bastien, hurriedly put them into shape, arranging them around a rose garden. This was to be known in future as the Clos Fleuri, or "flowered cloister."

From then on the Emmaus Home became a focal point of international friendship. The first young foreign visitors arrived on bicycles or made their way by hitchhiking: Finns, Austrians, Mexicans, Greeks, Hindus. In Africa, America, Europe, in many congresses and conferences, they had heard about the priest. These long-limbed youths spent a night, sometimes a week, sleeping in double-tiered beds in the dormitories, pitching their tents in the park, or sleeping in the open under the stars. On some evenings as many as 150 of them would gather together, singing in every language. The wonderful atmosphere they created delighted the priest. It brought back the fervor of his camping days, and he saw that these boys realized their responsible role in the world's future.

Their creed was based on a belief that the spirit of fraternity in their individual countries could conquer the spirit of hate. They were not political technicians. They dreamed of a union of all peoples, the realization of which would be more rapid and more realistic than that of the United Nations, because it would be based on other truths. Abbé Pierre himself had expressed on several occasions (in particular in a preface to a work on Gandhi and Tolstoi by A. Kaplan) a declaration of the principle of real world understanding:

"Great thinkers believe that what counts in life is the entire

community, the universe in its plenitude. But all of them, openly
or in secret, think that it is through *the sacrifice of others* that
this can be accomplished.

"Whenever a man, poor and daring as Christ, Tolstoi, or
Gandhi, stands up and without fear reminds men that universal
joy is only attained through *the sacrifice of oneself* and not
through that of the next man, he is mocked, he is insulted,
jailed, and, as a final touch, he is killed in the belief that through
death his doctrine will be abolished.

"It is not so much the differences between men that cause
wars, but those traits in men which are common and false.

"It is not through mobilized violence that one can change
people or bring about peace, but through violence to oneself—
the violence necessary to learn oneself, know oneself, to be true
to oneself. Then and only then can the masses change, can peace
be a reality.

"The sacrifices of individuals and nations . . .

"To pursue service for others rather than personal gain . . .

"Consent to the mutual limitation of sovereignties, first of all
of economic, territorial, and ideological sovereignties. . . ."

Immediately after the armistice these dreams seemed attain-
able. A few years were sufficient, however, for these generous im-
pulses to bog down in the bad faith and cunning of diplomats,
in the greed of national interests, or in uncompromising ideolo-
gies.

But in the summer of '49, when the priest was able to sit and
talk to a Czech and a Hindu student in the blossoming rose
garden or round the campfire in the park, the reason why he
had been brought here seemed clear to him. He felt that the
peace inspiring his young companions was sufficient to give a
spirit to this Home, and that this spirit would go with them
when they left, that it would stand as a symbol. However, the
significance of Emmaus was not limited merely to the idea of
faith in universal brotherhood, for Emmaus also stood as a symbol of the reality of suffering.

And suffering, as such, never ceased to loiter around the
Home. Soon it made brutal invasions.

The first autumn rains came. The youngsters hitched their
knapsacks on their backs and left, singly, or in groups, on motor-

cycles, bicycles, or on foot, to the four corners of the earth. Raindrops fell on the cinders of the campfire, and the roses of the "flowered cloister" lost their petals. . . .

Bastien, the lonely one, tidied the camp buildings, raked the dead leaves from the courtyard and under the trees, and carried stones and earth in his wheelbarrow to fill up holes in the ground left by the campers. Pieces of their huts, beams, and panels lay in piles on the ground awaiting their fate.

The priest planned to build a chapel back in the park, and since Bastien could not manage this work alone, when he could snatch an hour Abbé Pierre would lend him a hand. The soil at the end of the garden was rotting with gravel and plaster, so the foundation of the chapel would have to be built on concrete stilts. Iron piles must be driven in the ground and then the concrete would be poured over them.

One Saturday afternoon Bastien saw a man approaching the gates. He was stout, jovial in appearance, fortyish, and well dressed.

"I have offered the Father to help him with his work. We're neighbors. Since I work every other week on the night shift, I could come during those weeks and give you a hand half a day if you'd like."

"O.K."

"My name is Mathieu."

Bastien was not inquisitive. He didn't care what the man did for a living. But he had offered to help Emmaus "for free," and he had two good, strong arms.

Several days later another footstep on the gravel. Bastien saw a youth of not more than fifteen approaching in the rain. Bareheaded and coatless, shivering in his light wet jacket, he looked exhausted. His shoes and trousers were covered with slimy mud as though he had been walking through the fields.

"What do you want? What can I do for you?"

"I want to see the Father."

"The priest is just leaving for the Chamber of Deputies. He won't have much time."

But the priest took the time to hear the boy's story. Two years ago young Étienne had stolen a bicycle. Caught, he had been put in a reformatory but had escaped. Since then he had wandered round the suburbs, picking up fallen fruit from the orchards, sleeping against the wall of a house. He was an orphan, penniless, with nowhere to go. But nothing would induce him to return to the reform school.

"If you take me back, I'll only run away again."

"How did you get here?"

"I used to hike around and stay at the Youth Hostels. I saw your sign. I'm just a bum. Don't have a sou, but I can work."

The priest was pensive a moment.

"So it was by chance that you found your way."

"Yes."

"Tell me, Étienne, why did you confide in me? Why did you tell me of the reform school?"

The embarrassed boy murmured:

"I don't know why, Father, I don't know why."

"I asked you no questions. You could have just come to me and asked for a bed."

"Yes, but I had no money."

"You must be hungry. Bastien will get you something to eat and give you a couple of blankets. Wait a minute. I will try to do something about your case. You come under the jurisdiction of the V tribunal?"

"Yes."

"Then it's Judge N. who handled your case?"

"Yes. Are you going to turn me over to him?"

"I know him. But wait. This can all be worked out. Sometimes being a deputy serves a purpose."

It took two minutes over the telephone to arrange everything.

"I think the best way would be for you to keep him with you, Father," said the judge of the children's tribunal. "At least that way I don't have to worry. But officially I know nothing. I will even have the search continued for some time . . . for example, toward Bordeaux. Just give me the time to file the case."

Then on the first of November Djibouti appeared.

4: Djibouti and Bastien
The Man from Cité Rambaud

Now that he had come this far, Djibouti, leaning against the railing in the silence of the quiet, dark avenue, felt an immense fatigue. At the point of crossing this unknown threshold he was more conscious of his tired body than he'd ever been walking the streets of Paris, for that in itself was a form of distraction. But here at the end of the road, in the cold night, he seemed to be beyond life. The silence and the peace were too much. He was rendered unto himself, given back. . . .

To be rendered unto oneself. That was enough to scare anyone. The thought made him giddy. Leaning his head on the icy railing, Djibouti felt empty and physically spent. He shook with fever and was overcome by a paralyzing dismay, disgusted at the thought of having to beg once again for shelter and a bowl of soup. This nausea, this momentary pride, this uncontrollable revolt sometimes caused him to prefer sleeping in the open to begging for a bed. But now he was cold, hungry, and dead tired. And the stinging pain in his leg . . . Once again he was in the pitiful position of one who must receive rather than one who gives, the privilege of the rich.

In this state of torpor he was barely conscious of a voice singing in the cellar. The voice was young, with a slight drawl:

"Star of the Snows, dry your lovely eyes . . ."

Djibouti pulled himself together, tugged at his clothes. That is to say he set his cap straight and turned down his coat collar. He always hated giving the impression of a derelict, and especially on a day like today when he felt particularly low and at the end of his rope.

He repeated "Emmaus." The name had obsessed him all the way, in the subway and in the bus. It seemed to bring back something—something a long way off, and mysterious, as everything appeared now when it came from his childhood or from religion. Maybe it was a hostel like the Salvation Army, where they sang a hymn before supper. But tonight, would he be the only boarder? It all seemed so deserted. And now this unexpected song:

> *"And when the sunny days would come again*
> *Back to the village he'd go."*

He discovered a flight of steps to the left of the building and went down, guided by the boy's voice.

Through a cemented basement and through a dark room, where a table and chairs were dimly in view. Light shone from a door in the back and from there, too, came the smell of cooking.

"*Bonsoir*," said Djibouti.

"*Bonsoir*," replied young Étienne, busy cutting up potatoes. There was oil sizzling in a skillet on a small stove, the chimney of which ran out the window.

"I have been sent by . . ."

"Who the hell cares?" said Étienne. "Do you want to see the priest?"

"I want to sleep. Have you room for me?"

"There's always plenty of room. The Father will be along soon. But Mademoiselle is there. She's the secretary."

Djibouti shrugged his shoulders. Étienne looked at him, screwed up his brow, and smiled.

"You haven't eaten," he said.

"No."

"Fine. Supper isn't ready yet, but get yourself a glass in the meantime. Smoke?"

"No," said Djibouti.

He sat down. He noticed in the badly lit room three camp beds and a straw mattress on the floor.

"*Tiens,* here he comes," exclaimed the boy.

The headlights of a car flashed across the stairway, wheels churned the gravel in the court.

"Come," said Étienne.

Two iron bedsteads were tied to the luggage rack on the car. The slim bearded priest, stooping slightly, wore a beret and a leather windbreaker over his cassock. He was busy untying knots.

"You're just in time, Étienne," he said. "Here are the beds for Mohamed and his friend."

"Father, we have a guest," said Étienne.

"I was sent by . . ." Djibouti started to say.

The priest looked at him. The headlights shining on the vagabond's face accentuated the irregular features. His eyes met the priest's—and he knew he would be accepted into the Home.

"Careful," said the priest. "The bed is sliding off. Can you hang on to one corner? Help me carry it down to the basement."

When the beds were put in place:

"Thank you," the priest said, and stretched out his hand to Djibouti. "Forgive me for having put you to work in this way."

And this was the way in which Djibouti became a member of the Emmaus community.

Next morning he saw the priest, just as he was about to leave for the Chamber.

"Thinking of leaving?" said the priest. "Do you have anywhere to go?"

Djibouti shrugged his shoulders.

"You can stay here if you want to. You can help us by giving the others a hand. They'll tell you about it."

That day and the next Djibouti worked with Étienne and Bastien laying the cement foundation of a small bungalow between the yard and the park, and he moved in with them in the basement along with two Arabs who worked in town and came to Emmaus only in the evenings. Djibouti saw the priest not more than two or three times a week in passing. But little by little the way this man had accepted him so simply, in such brotherly fashion, with such spontaneous trust, began giving him food for thought. Étienne and Bastien spoke little of themselves and for a long time he knew nothing of their past. But in the evenings they explained the Father to him.

"As far as he's concerned, any poor devil is as good as another, and anyway there are no poor devils for him. He cares nothing about our past. But he doesn't expect us to lie to him."

"I'll stay one week," Djibouti said to himself. But when the date approached he felt himself seized by panic. For the first time solitude terrorized him. And there was something else, too. In spite of the fact that he saw the priest so seldom, he hated to leave him. He had often thought that by his work he was helping him and that the priest would be happy to see the progress they had made around the place. He felt also that he, Djibouti, would not be under complete obligation this way.

He knew he was not a fast worker. His gestures were a little slow, sometimes clumsy. But he could do all right if he wasn't bullied and was given time to finish his job. Even if gardening wasn't his special dish, he was putting his heart into it.

Bastien wasn't much of a talker either, but he was always in a fairly good humor. Étienne, the boy, was different, a bit restless, sometimes bragging, sowing wild oats. All were free, uninhibited, without any fear of tomorrow. The team got along all right, so Djibouti said to himself, "Why don't I stay right here?"

Saturday afternoons and Sundays youth groups came and settled either in the inn or in the second-floor rooms reserved for families. They held their meetings in the large room of the small lodge in the courtyard.

"Christian workers," said Bastien.

To Djibouti, these words seemed to be contradictory. Religion seemed to him to be the business of the bourgeois, of simple peasants, of women and children, of gullible people exploited by the Church. The very existence of a priest like Abbé Pierre was disconcerting. Here was a man of superior spirit charged with high functions, a specialist in social problems, attuning his political views with his faith and his charity, and remaining very human, very simple, very close to the "little people."

He respected you and did not try to convert you without asking you first whether you were hungry. He was truly sincere.

One evening as they were lying on their beds of straw down in the basement Djibouti heard Bastien sobbing. He had come home drunk, and his drunkenness was of a sullen and taciturn kind. Étienne was sleeping. Outside, rain was pelting the gravel. Over this background noise Djibouti could hear the clatter of Mademoiselle's typewriter. Abbé Pierre was in his office dictating letters.

Finally Djibouti could stand it no longer. The tearing sobs, stifled under the covers, were dreadful upheavals of a sorrow so deep that even wine could not pacify it.

"Hey, Bastien!"

There was no answer. (My sorrow is my own. My dead, my remorse. I don't offer it to friends as you would a drink or a smoke. If I'd known I would have been better off to stay in prison . . .)

"Bastien . . ."

"Leave me alone."

And then after a silence Bastien came out with it all.

"Do you want to know how it happened? Do you want to know how I killed my uncle?"

Djibouti was scared. "Don't tell me unless you want to. I'm not asking for it."

But it was too late. By now Bastien had to get this nightmare out of his system. In a voice hoarse and stumbling he wrenched out from his agonizing and bloody past the incoherent shreds of the story.

Fields of flax, acres of flax and beets, up there in the north, not far from the Belgian border. This was the land that Bastien, then only fifteen and an orphan, was to inherit when he came of age. In the hall hung his uncle's gun, a great, black customs inspector's revolver. And Lucie. Lucie, the girl from Gravelines whom Bastien loved and wanted to marry. The deserted windy dunes, too, where the young people would meet on warm summer evenings. And that woman. That horrible, vulgar, stingy woman. A widow with two sons his old uncle had married, and, of course, she hated Bastien, future master of the estate. She moved into the house with her father and her mother, and they, too, hated Bastien. All their gossip and their mischief-making were aimed at provoking a quarrel between the young, betrothed couple. Anything to get Bastien out of the way and keep him out of the way. Then the accident, a falling rafter. Only she, such a woman, could have imagined it to be an attempt at murder. This horrified Bastien, and he wanted to scare her. He reached for the ancient revolver, loaded it . . . "No, no, I swear I didn't aim at him. Why should I want to kill him, my uncle?" The inquest followed with the trumped-up evidence, the verdict, then the departure for Cayenne.[1] After twenty years of hard labor it was an old man who came back. He returned to the north, but Lucie was married. Bewildered, desperate, weary, and disgusted, he renounced all ownership to his property. Helpless and unadvised, considered an intruder by all, he finally wound up in Paris in a small hotel close to Emmaus—and there he took out his razor.

By chance the hotel proprietor came by in the nick of time; and at wit's end, he called up Abbé Pierre, whom he knew. The priest rushed over and immediately offered Bastien a place at Emmaus. Slowly the wounds healed, and little by little Bastien regained his courage and the desire to live. Work, the friendship of Abbé Pierre, the responsibilities he now assumed in the upkeep of the inn and estate, all these brought him some peace of mind. On certain evenings, though, his despair overcame him, choked him; and alone in the dark, under his covers, he struggled against it.

Outside, the rain continued to fall regularly. Upstairs could still be heard the clatter of the typewriter and Abbé Pierre's voice like an appeasing whisper.

Soon all was silent. His political work at an end for the day, the priest prayed for those close to him who were in torment. In accepting this responsibility for bodies and souls he was simply continuing the mission revealed to him in his childhood.

When he thought of Djibouti and Bastien, the priest saw in them the spirit of a man he had known as a child in the Cité Rambaud. It was an old, very old memory. The same face, filled with a faded strength; the prematurely aged features revealing a latent will which did not wear out with time, but suddenly failed under the stress of disaster. The eyes did not beg for pity. Deep down this man had not accepted failure as his lot. He was

[1] France's equivalent for Alcatraz.

still burning with the fever of those who refuse to adapt to their miserable condition; who are not grateful for a service rendered but must acquit themselves by paying it back with an equal service. The beneficiary claims the right to be a benefactor in his turn, and to give good for good.

The priest recalled the scene. He was then but twelve years old. His father on that particular Sunday had taken him by the hand. In the other one he carried a small suitcase. Every Sunday his father had gone away like this, and young Henri, though intrigued, had never dared ask any questions about these mysterious absences.

His father kept a rendezvous, a date with poverty. Like silk manufacturing, poverty was one of Lyons' specialties. In the squalid slums of the Croix Rousse district, in the windowless rooms where doctors and nursing nuns hardly dared penetrate, solitary men and women thrown out of overcrowded hospitals and even entire families were huddled, perishing with cold and hunger.

In order to struggle with so much despair the city of Lyons, cradle of Christian social welfare, could only multiply her works of mercy. Among these, the foundation of *hospitaliers-veilleurs* enlisted in its early days men willing to sit at night with poor, homeless souls who had died without families. This tradition had faded out little by little, but now the *hospitaliers* (among whom were to be found manufacturers like Henri's father, owners of silk mills, high functionaries of the city) went anonymously several hours every Sunday to care for the poor of the city.

Of course the boy was unaware of all this. He had never yet looked upon a real beggar.

"Where are we going, Papa?"

"To the Cité Rambaud, in the Brotteaux district."

Around the church there was a group of small houses built by a priest for aged workmen and their families. Having no other place to meet, it was customary for the *hospitaliers* to receive the poor of the city, the ragpickers, beggars, and tramps in the dining hall of the church rectory.

No, until that evening young Henri had never made contact with misery. On Sundays in the corner of the church porch a

beggar would smile at him or thank him, when, coming from
Mass, he would give the poor man a few charitable sous. But the
smile and the "thank you" of the old man belonged in a way to
his existence as a rich man's son. Had he ever played with or
spoken to a poor man's child? Had he ever entered a poor man's
home? Had he ever gone walking in the teeming slum districts
of his own city? No. He vaguely knew that there was a world of
misery somewhere, but subconsciously he associated the misfortune of the poor with wrongdoing and evil.

This confused idea was rarely expressed out loud but rather
implied under one's breath. So always in this bourgeois milieu,
where charity was practical but was based on principles of self-
sufficiency, it could be summarized thus: Good fortune is the
natural (and quasi-providential) reward of the virtuous social
class. It confers dignity and attracts respectability. A man's worth
is judged by his fortune. A poor man is one suffering from some
defect if not some vice. The beggars, those whose hunted look
the child had caught, were part of an entirely different group
of human beings than the one to which he belonged. If they
were poor, they were a danger and a threat. One could expect
anything from hobos—theft, rape, murder. They were but
wolves in men's clothing.

And suddenly here he was, right in their midst. There were
about forty of them in this large room. Odd-looking people with
their clothes in rags—and smelling to high heaven. What kind
of horrible trap had Papa fallen into?

But as if unconscious of danger, his father was speaking to
them with ease. He was talking to them as he would to humans,
smiling at them and even shaking their hands. Happily Henri
recognized several gentlemen whom he had seen in his home,
gentlemen of considerable civic importance. But he couldn't
imagine why they were compromising their dignity with these
ragged tramps.

"Come along, son, stop dreaming! Will you go and fill this
jug with water?"

Outside in the court Henri did some thinking while the water
ran into the jug. Standing under the spring sky, he began to understand what all the gentlemen were doing there, and what
cause drew his father to these meetings. How wonderful it was

to be good. And an intense interest urged the child to return, to help these fine gentlemen, his father's friends, do good. He wanted to play his role of charitable little rich boy.

Now his father had turned barber. With his sleeves rolled up, wearing an apron and armed with a pair of scissors, he was trimming an old man's beard. A towel was tied round the man's neck. Henri at first was tempted to believe this was a scene in a play, or a game, and he smiled. But suddenly his eyes met those of the old man, and the look he saw there expressed in no way love or gratefulness for such kindness. The look was at one and the same time scared and insolent, cruel and demanding, a look that claimed this kind act as just due. How many times Henri was to meet this fearful and demanding look—the look of the suffering.

There was no way of telling whether Papa, too, had seen this savage look. He was talking in his usual mild manner and going on with the barbering.

But the man never relaxed, and the smile the child was waiting for never came. And it suddenly seemed to the boy that now it was his father who was the poor man, that he was the humble servant afraid of displeasing his master. Would his father get a smile from the miserable wretch or a word of satisfaction, of thanks? But the other kept silent, and his look was icy. The scissors flew around the ungrateful face.

"Will this do? How's that?" asked the stand-in barber.

"No, a little more at the sides," growled the man.

The child had heard them tell in church, "You must love your neighbor." That was an important commandment. This strange individual, "your neighbor," he had never met outside of his family. But here was this man—also a neighbor—and you were supposed to love him. And the others around here, dirty, vermin-infested beggars, drooling, smelling of wine, tobacco, and sweat, they, too, were neighbors in the image of Christ. This was no game. To his mind it was a shocking situation and there was no escaping it.

And then the tramp began to look like a human being. A man's face appeared from beneath the razor, and as the transformation continued, the hunted-beast look disappeared and was replaced by one of satisfied assurance. His father undid the towel. The man got up. At last he smiled and, stretching out his hand to Henri's father, said, "Thank you, sir. Now what can I do in return?"

"Why?" asked the father, nonplused.

"Well, to return the favor, in my turn."

"But, but, nothing, thank you. I really don't know."

On the way home, filled with thoughts of the unlimited greatness of charity in action, thoughts which both tempted and horrified him, the boy walked silently by his father's side. The latter moved slowly, his face drawn by the sickness which was soon to take his life.

"You noticed," he said, "this man wanted by all means to return the little favor I did him. And how awkward I was. It's very hard, Henri, to be worthy of those who suffer."

And he added these words which explained the dejection in which he returned home every Sunday, after the sessions in the Cité Rambaud:

"One can never get even with poverty. One pretends to do something, but one should give himself completely, plunge into it body and soul, like a grain of wheat in dark earth."

5: The Kangaroo
The Chapel

A<small>RE</small> you hiring anyone here?"
"I'm not the boss," Étienne answered the stranger. "You'll have to see the Father."
"Where do I find him?"
"At the Pope's. In Rome."
Louis the Kangaroo was not a bad fellow really. He just wouldn't have his leg pulled. Since his last jail term he had become quite short-tempered. He said to himself that when you have twenty years' boxing experience behind you, it's just too bad you don't get the chance to put this science into practice on some of these smart youngsters. This viewpoint, however, was not shared by the police. In fact, it led him to a term in the Pontoise prison. But still, no one must take any liberties with him.
Étienne was not joking at all. Serenely he looked his shabby companion in the face and repeated:
"The Father is in Rome, I'm telling you. Go see Mademoiselle. She's his secretary."
The Kangaroo stayed at Emmaus. When the priest returned from Rome, where he had been received by the Pope in a private audience, he heard the story of Louis the Kangaroo.
"I must tell you, Father . . ."
"If you want to. But I am not asking you any questions."
Oh, how he needed someone to confide in, the poor lost youth.

45

For him as for the others coming to Emmaus for help the down-
fall happened simply, an almost natural decline. Social inadapt-
ability, the awkwardness characteristic of the poor, struggling to
live, alcohol, and the sinister push downward given by war,
years of prison camp—this was an almost identical replica of
Djibouti's story.

Yet at the start Louis the Kangaroo had had a turn of good
luck stemming from his well-developed biceps. He was not just
a district boxer—hadn't the papers mentioned him twice. One
reporter actually said that, "His dry swing and footwork were
like that of a Kangaroo." That meant nothing, of course, but the
nickname had stuck, and tucked away in his billfold Louis had
the two clippings, yellowed with age.

His sporting career in Paris did not last long. The main reason was a young woman who encouraged his physical dissipa-
tion. So he toured the provinces as a sparring partner. Then
came the war and prison camp. On his return he found he had
lost both his girl friend and his famous footwork. So from one
boxing ring to another he wandered, teaching beginners, and,
finally, sweeping the arena and maintaining the equipment. He
had to breathe the dust, the leather, the sweat of the sporting
club. And gradually, "to keep in shape," he started taking dope.
This evicted him from the training clubs, a poor fallen Kangaroo.
So he took to hanging around pubs, meeting "old has-beens" of
his own generation. These decrepit sons of a noble art, his only
family, had become "available," like himself, for any kind of
match.

Then came a fight where Louis knocked out his partner,
fought with the police like a madman, and got six months in
jail. At forty-three, with his raucous voice, his broken nose, red
face, thick eyelids, and his low brow deeply furrowed with worry
lines, he looked much older than his age. But in his great body
he maintained a reserve of muscular force which, after all the
alcohol, has retained a nostalgia for intense effort and a desire to
be of use.

"Yes, remain with us," said the Father. "But remember, for
your comrades' sake and for young Étienne, as well as for the
others who live here or visit us on Sundays, I do not want you
to be seen when you have been drinking."

"I promise you, Father . . ."

"No, you don't have to promise anything. This is a request. Make an effort. Otherwise, I will not be able to keep you."

"Maybe I was a little hard," thought Abbé Pierre to himself as he left him, "but I must have some discipline in the house."

Suddenly he stopped short. The word "house." It had come quite naturally, as a habit. To this man, as well as to Bastien, Djibouti, and young Étienne, it stood for something not just symbolic, but extremely concrete. For them there was no other refuge in the world. Emmaus had become a thriving community with an almost family atmosphere.

From then on the house developed a new destiny. It soon became a hearth for other unfortunate men, for instance, two North Africans whose eyes burned with dignified despair and an immense capacity for suffering—two of the innumerable mass of North Africans lost in Paris who, when they had a little money, were easy game for exploiters, and who, when broke, could be bought for practically nothing.

Despite the cold the Kangaroo wore only a light shirt with his tattered corduroy trousers. He swung his sledge hammer, wham—down it came on an iron pile.

Wham! "for their ugly mugs . . ."

The Father had gone off with Étienne and Bastien to get some cement. Djibouti was busy sawing planks near the dormitory. Only the mysterious neighbor, Monsieur Mathieu, was working with the Kangaroo this Saturday afternoon. Several youngsters who had come for a meeting were singing in the big hall of the Youth Hostel.

Wham! The shock of the heavy hammer against the pile snapped the air like a rifle shot.

Wham! "for the dirty pigs in the State Police . . ."

The pole sank into the soft ground—one more pile for the chapel foundation. A few feet away Mathieu was clearing the ground with his spade. Every time the Kangaroo brought down his hammer and damned the guardians of law and order, Monsieur Mathieu winced.

Wham! "for the dirty police in the fifteenth *arrondissement* . . ."

6: *Build!*

"T HEY can't do that to us. They can't throw a family with children out on the street."

In a letter of just eight lines the catastrophe of immediate eviction came to knock on the door of the clerk of the Paris Hotel, a modest establishment on the national highway just a little over a mile from Emmaus. And in their complete despair this man and his wife overlooked the fact that more than once they themselves, though through no fault of their own, had put tenants out on the street or had refused a room in their overcrowded hotel to wandering families.

"No, he can't do that to us," repeated the woman.

"You know very well we have no contract," said the husband.

"Go to the union. Get a lawyer."

But no scheming, no desperate consultation could in any way alter the fact. Raoul was not even a tenant in the hotel, but only an employee of the proprietor who had "authorized" him to occupy a three-room flat for himself, his wife, his three children, and the grandparents.

And of course with the loss of the flat he lost the job also. All this in a single stroke, and they had no savings set aside.

"I could just weep," Jeanne, the wife, kept repeating, dazed by the hopelessness of their lot.

Finally she talked her husband into going to see the proprietor in Clichy.

"Explain the situation. He'll understand."

50

And the proprietor did understand perfectly, but he was help-less to do anything. He had decided to enlarge the Paris Hotel, to transform it into a plush establishment, and to take over the running of it himself. He gave Raoul a week's notice.

"I could live in two rooms."

"Impossible. They must all be emptied for the workmen."

On his return Raoul rushed to the employment office and then to the Prefecture of Police to put his name down in the "Apartments Wanted" section.

"We'll write you the minute we have anything."

The grandmother never ceased moaning and weeping. On the sixth day Raoul sold his furniture to a secondhand dealer, keep-ing just his straw mattresses. The few knickknacks and trinkets they possessed he pawned at the Mont de Piété. On the morning of the eighth day the proprietor's car stopped at the door. He said guardedly:

"I have ordered the masons and painters for tomorrow morn-ing. Have you found anything yet? . . . No?"

He handed them five 1000-franc notes. Raoul took two rooms at the nearest hotel.

"All we'll be able to afford is five days," moaned the wife. "Then what'll we do? Put Grandma and Grandpa in a home? Send the children to the Public Assistance? And ourselves, can we go to the Salvation Army for help?"

During the afternoon, as she was telling her story to the dairy people, one of the clients who did washing in the Emmaus neigh-borhood mentioned the great house belonging to Abbé Pierre.

The next night the family was installed at Emmaus.

"Just for a few days, Monsieur l'Abbé." (In all, they spent eleven months there.)

The priest installed them in the tiny bungalow on the left of the court, where, while waiting for the chapel to be finished, he had said Mass. He had to move his altar and the Blessed Sacra-ment to another part of the building.

He said later: "God was the first to give up His place to the homeless."

A short while after Raoul got a job in the maintenance de-partment of the Paris subway. During that winter Djibouti, Bastien, the Kangaroo, and young Étienne finished the chapel, lifted the level of the court at Clos Fleuri, pulled down more prisoners' huts in Saint-Denis, and, having transported them in bits and pieces to Emmaus, built new dormitories and small rooms. The priest had planned only to enlarge Emmaus for the groups and married couples who came for week-ends and for the Youth Groups who came during the summer for retreats. Still, there was a surplus of materials—enough to build even a small lodge.

"Father," said the ex-policeman Mathieu to the priest one day, "I see you have some building material left over. Would you let me have it?"

"What for? Are you planning to build?"

"Well, I just got an eviction notice. My landlord won't renew my lease. I was thinking that if I could find a bit of land, not too expensive . . ."

The priest asked Raoul, the ex-clerk, if this idea of building a house of his own might not interest him, too.

"But, Father, how can I pay for it? And where will I find any property?"

"Don't worry, my parliamentary salary will solve that. You can repay me in installments."

They talked things over with a real-estate agent who offered them a piece of land in the same district, about two miles from Emmaus, in a place called La Barrière.

In this way, almost by chance, the first housing project came into being. It was a small-scale prototype of the future Emergency Cities.

While all this was going on the priest was too absorbed by his parliamentary duties to give much of his own time, but he gave them the inspiration, drew up plans, filed a request for a building permit, advanced the money, and asked the men at Emmaus to help the two families with their building.

At Emmaus, and particularly at the Youth Hostel, there was much to be done in the way of organization and upkeep. This fell mainly to the lot of Bastien and Étienne, but whenever they had any free time they would join Djibouti and the Kangaroo on the Barrière project.

The lot was a bit of wasteland bordered with hawthorn bushes and set amid the vegetable growers' plots. Its name came from a railway crossing. Under four hundred yards away a secondary railroad running from the great plants along the riverbank joined the main Arsenal line. Often, when pausing to stretch their aching backs, the men watched the slow freight trains filled with minerals or machinery go by. Farther down, between the rooftops and green trees, they could glimpse the river where barges glided by and small fishing boats clustered around the banks.

They broke ground for the new houses in April, even before they had legal permission to build. Theoretically, French law requires that water mains, sewage systems, and preliminary electrical lines must be installed before actual construction can begin. But the Companions of Emmaus started everything at the same time. While skilled laborers were helping them lay water lines and electric cables they were going ahead with laying the foundations and cementing cellar walls. Raoul and Mathieu came to help in the evenings when they returned from working in the city. Occasionally the priest's car would appear round the bend of the road and Abbé Pierre, accompanied by an architect friend, would get out, give directions, and often wield shovel, pickax, and hammer.

To guard the tools from theft, Djibouti volunteered to sleep on the lot in a tent. The two months he spent there seemed to assuage his chronic bitterness—and something else happened to him, too. On the edge of the field, surrounded by the blossoming hawthorn, stood a little tree—a poplar. From his tent Djibouti watched it burst into a spray of tender green leaves. He, who had renounced everything that belonged to the outside world, who had applied himself for years to stifling all feeling, experienced a thrill of wonder in listening to the rustle of the young tree overhead. Then the wind would fall, the whisper would become almost imperceptible, a tugboat would blow its whistle on the river, an automobile horn would be heard on the road. And suddenly the mobile little leaves would be animated again, and would lap the light breeze just as a small animal might do in drinking.

One morning he found a puppy, barely a few weeks old and still shaky on his little paws, wandering around the basement of the new building. He was a mongrel—a cross between an Alsatian sheep dog and a common mutt. He had long ears and a black patch over one eye. Djibouti fed him, and the puppy attached himself with desperate adoration to the man. Djibouti asked the priest for permission to keep him and named him "Finaud"—Smartie.

On summer evenings, his body aching after a hard day's work on the house, Djibouti cooked his simple meal over a campfire. Then he would sit under the tree, the dog at his feet, and watch night fall over the valley. Lights came on along the riverbank, in the suburban houses and little inns. Red lights danced behind the dark glass roofs of the factories. Djibouti felt that at last he was at peace with himself and the world. He felt *really* free. He had never known how to use his so-called freedom when roaming the streets of Paris. But this liberty was now of a different sort —in a sense he was free because he had given up freedom—and should the Father ask him to give up even more to help at Emmaus, he would.

But on some evenings, sitting under the whispering little tree with his dog, so much security made Djibouti uneasy. He would suddenly feel guilty for being so far removed from life, sheltered as he now was from all torment. He felt somehow that he had to pay for this peace, or at least deserve it through still harder work.

One morning early in June a new man whom Abbé Pierre had picked up arrived on the lot with Bastien, Mathieu, and the Kangaroo. He was a great, strapping fellow who gave his name as Baptiste. Who was he? Where was he from? He spoke little, and according to the rules no one asked him anything about his past.

Two weeks later, sitting in the shade of the building where the men were finishing their meal, Baptiste pointed to the train slowly rolling away from the factory, and said:

"Jeeps. And trucks mounted with machine guns. Two to a flatcar. That makes at least 200 in the last half-hour."

Then after a short silence:

"A jeep built for war costs more than a house—that makes a whole village that has gone by—a town of 3,000 people."

"There have to be jeeps and armored trucks, too," said Mathieu.

Baptiste said no more, but kept sullenly silent.

Several days later, when his comrades were starting back to Emmaus, Baptiste said he would rather stay on the lot and that he would sleep under the stars close by Djibouti's tent.

"I can make room for you in the tent," said Djibouti.

"No, I don't like sleeping cooped up, even in a tent."

So, rolled up in a blanket, he stretched himself on the ground outside the tent. On the fifth day, as night was falling, the two men sat side by side under the little whispering tree with the dog at their feet. Both were silent, breathing the strong fragrance of the flowers in the field and neighboring gardens. Their eyes wandered lazily over the peaceful valley and up to the great sky where one by one the stars were coming out. Baptiste was smoking a cigarette. He said pensively:

"This is the first time in my life that I've done any building."

"Same here," said Djibouti.

"No, but with me it's different. You see, until now all I had learned was to the contrary. Demolish, destroy. Destroy and kill. I have never learned anything else; not since I was fifteen. Then I was the regimental mascot. I was twenty-two when France fell. Then I went underground to the *maquis*, then the F.F.I. [Free French Resistance]—Alsace, Germany, Occupation. . . . You will ask me why I didn't get demobilized? But I've just told you, all I know is fighting, and I was caught in the circle. Indo-China, that was the last straw.

"I don't want to get into the question of just or unjust wars. I don't give a damn about politics. But now I know, I know it under my skin, that war is the greatest evil. To hate and kill, try to hate as much as you can because our enemies hate and are trying to kill us. Hate enough to have courage to parachute out of a plane in order to destroy and kill there where we fell. We were well paid and decorated, too. And the money went fast on drink, drugs, and women. I caught the fever, and then my efficiency rating as a killer went down and the same outfit that had appointed me to kill threw me out.

"One year ago I was repatriated. At Marseille they welcomed us with a fanfare. That was glory, we were heroes, we were being used to recruit other two-cent heroes and after that . . . Well, what the hell? I went back to my family in Normandy. My brothers who had gotten rich in the black market during the occupation said to me: 'You should have done what we did.' I smashed all the crockery, and went off to Paris. After I went through my bonus I was a derelict. There was only one way out. That was suicide. A lady in the Red Cross gave me Abbé Pierre's name. Living near him, maybe I can still learn to do something useful, build instead of pulling down. Love, maybe. . . ."

He lit another cigarette and laughed self-consciously at having spoken so frankly.

"Here I am telling you all this . . ."

"I understand," said Djibouti.

To the west lay dark hills sprinkled with lights, and above them could be seen the great glow reflected by the Paris sky. In the distance was a muffled rumbling. Crickets were chirping in the grass near the two men; they sat in silence, and over their heads a warm breeze blowing in light gusts whispered in the young poplar tree.

"Peace," murmured Baptiste. "I used to think a long time ago that to be a man you had to be stronger than anyone else. That's what they'd always taught me. In the talk I had with the Father the day I got here, he said, 'Strength, yes, but not to dominate. To protect, to defend justice and truth, at the service of everyone. It's because no one understands this simple truth that there's so much misery in this world.' "

In the beginning it was planned that the Barrière project would consist of two lodges, each with two two-room apartments. They would be made of prefab wooden sections placed on stone basements. The lodges would measure thirty by twenty feet and have a tin roof. But just before the building that was to house Raoul and Mathieu and their families was finished, Abbé Pierre appeared on the lot with a new plan in hand.

"We have leftover panels and material," he said. "What a pity not to be able to use everything. The lot would permit enlarging the building."

From the beginning of the work, rumors had flown around that neither public works nor large contractors had succeeded in building cheap apartments that were worth living in but that the priest and his Companions were managing to do this. At this news new families had applied to him for lodging instead of to the city's social welfare centers. Without ado the team started digging the foundation for another building measuring seventy-five feet in length that would contain five apartments. The new expenses quickly ate up all of Abbé Pierre's meager budget. A few mornings later Baptiste and Djibouti saw approaching the lot a weird vehicle, an antique Mona-6—a French car comparable to the Model-T Ford. The driver sat on a high platform, the whole body of the car towering above the earth on spoked wheels. To the rear was attached a trailer. The contraption pulled up, and out of it stepped Abbé Pierre.

"But, Father . . . your sedan? . . ."

"Sold this morning, exchanged for this wonderful deal. Look at the style! Greatest wonder is that she goes! All we need now is my deputy's tricolor. What a sensation she'll be at the Palais Bourbon. Seriously, though, think of the materials we can haul on this trailer."

And the ancient vehicle did delight the French parliamentarians whenever the priest parked it in the court of the National Assembly, and it certainly rendered a great service to the builders on the lot.

One morning the priest came by in his jalopy to pick up Djibouti, Baptiste, and Bastien to haul a load of building material. They loaded the truck with bricks, and Djibouti and Baptiste, worn with fatigue, piled on top for the ride back. The old car noisily crossed Paris and at noontime reached the Place de l'Opéra. There a traffic jam caught them in the middle of the intersection where two policemen were directing traffic; and the engine died. Djibouti jumped down to crank it. The light turned green but the car would not start. Behind, a long line of cars started honking impatiently. One of the policemen whistled and walked indignantly toward them.

Suddenly he stopped dead. He had noticed the deputy's cockade on the windshield. The priest's smiling face further disconcerted him; but, still, it must be a hoax.

"What's all this? A joke? Where are your papers?"

The priest produced his card. The expression on the cop's face changed into a beaming smile. His eyes went from the card to the Father's Legion of Honor and then to the cockade on the jalopy.

"So it's you, Abbé—uhh—Deputy. Well, let me congratulate you. Allow me to shake your hand. I've wanted to meet you for a long time."

His comrade on the traffic platform, the passers-by, the honking cars behind them witnessed with wonder the strange scene of a policeman grinning broadly and shaking the hand of the strange bearded traveler in the strange beaten car.

Then, by some miracle, the car started up, as though it realized that the humor of the situation should not be spoiled by further delay.

On a July morning the building team observed two dark-skinned youths approaching.

"We are Hindu students in Paris, and we wish to spend a few days at Emmaus. The priest has told us about the lot. What can we do?"

Three days later a Dane, a Belgian, an Australian, and two Englishmen joined the workers. As last year, the summer guests, the husky barelegged youths, arrived, too. The priest told them about the work in progress. Immediately they offered their aid, willingly giving up their excursions in Paris to join the ex-hobos on the building lot. But now the tramps had become specialized workers, and it was they who assigned the various jobs. Youths representing fourteen nations worked that summer to build houses for five French families.

Finally, when the roof was all that remained to be done, there appeared on the scene an official controller, yardstick in hand.

"The legal measurements for the frontage are thirty feet. I see that your façade measures seventy-five."

"True enough," said the priest. "In our enthusiasm we used up all the material we had. At first we had planned a house for only two families. In the meantime more homeless families arrived, so we made it as large as possible, to be exact, fifteen rooms."

"But the Ministry will never authorize . . ."

"Look," said the priest conciliatingly. "These families will willingly leave the premises, I can assure you. Provided, that is, that the Ministry can lodge them."

The controller folded up his yardstick and left, infuriated or touched by grace, who knows? No other conflict came to interrupt the completion of the building, the installation of facilities, and the moving of five families in September. And at the same time ground was broken on the plot for three new bungalows.

Experience had proved that from a beginning of practically nothing, that which appeared impossible could be realized. Here was a building worth 900,000 francs, built in a few short months, that included fifteen rooms and all essential conveniences. Why wait, then, while entire families wandered in the open, while children died outdoors on the street, and when so many men, young and old, were ready to go to work to save them?

But who could then foresee all the consequences of this first achievement?

7 : *The Influx of the Homeless*

JUNE 1951 saw the legislative elections in France. The priest refused to accept the support of certain parties and, consequently, gave up his seat in the Assembly.

He then decided to dedicate himself entirely to Emmaus. But with the loss of his parliamentary salary, the little community lost nearly all its regular income. There were still the friends of Emmaus who contributed voluntarily and the youth groups who paid rent for space, but at the same moment when material security started to crumble, the priest was assailed by more and more appeals for help. The first construction started after this brought to the poor little team of Emmaus workers far worse than administrative difficulties.

Some time later Abbé Pierre wrote:

"That which brutally, terribly, fell upon us, because we had built one house, was the cry of anguish emanating from throughout an immense region all around us, the pleading entreaty of the anonymous multitudes, for whom life had been rendered worse than death by the conditions in which they were obliged to exist."

A man crouched in the chair in the priest's office. He sobbed brokenly:

"We can't take it any longer . . ."

Michel worked on the same subway maintenance team as Raoul, the ex-hotel clerk.

"The Father can help. Go see him," Raoul had said to Michel one day.

Michel was young and strong. At twenty-six he had been married three years, had a nice wife, a child, and a room on the Rue du Temple—theoretically, all that is essential for happiness. Except that, in the room, there were nine people.

Only one room, almost entirely filled by two large beds and a mattress on the floor. Not even a sink. In one bed Michel and his wife slept with their child, Daniel. Sandwiched together in the other bed were the father, the mother, and Michel's divorced elder sister with her small son. There were also Michel's sister-in-law, a girl of fifteen, and her brother, nineteen. Both of them slept on the mattress.

The mother was an invalid and bedridden. Michel's wife nursed her all day while the others were working. The mother could no longer stand the cries of little Daniel and complained from morning to night. And when she was not moaning, she was quarrelsome, tyrannical, frenzied. She would not let them open the window, and the air in the room was thick and fetid, for she never changed clothes or bed linen and did not wash. In the beginning they had shared the housework and washing. Then there had been some semblance of order and discipline in this family community. Now, everything had broken down. When the young folks got home in the evening they either did not speak to one another or they quarreled. There were violent scenes starting from the least pretext, and each one shouted he would "get the hell out of here." Yet they all stayed, trapped, because no one of them had enough money to leave. The father of the family was weak, taciturn, and generally half drunk.

Michel, returning from work, would kiss his wife, his child, and say a general *"Bonsoir"* to the others. He would then ask his wife to send him shopping—anything rather than face the same terrible routine again. He knew he was a coward, but he just couldn't breathe the rotten air in this den where he, too, would end up by losing his mind.

He wondered how his wife could stand it. He would take little Daniel by the hand, and they would stroll to the end of the street, window-shopping. Then he would have a glass of wine at the corner bistro and slowly make his way home. The others would have finished their supper by the time he got back. He would rather eat his food cold and alone than get into discussions with his father and brother-in-law.

If petite Madame Michel seemed to take this hell quietly, it was because she hoped, because she lived in a dream. She saw a room, a tiny corner, where she could be alone with her husband and child—a door to which she would have a key. How she would polish, care for, and love this little home. There, everything would be spotless, everything would belong to her, to Daniel and to her husband. They would never have to see the filth of others, never smell anything like this room again; they would not have to listen to stupid chatter or awful noises.

But this dream would evaporate before the horror of reality. Oh, how violently one could hate one's husband's parents. How much one would like to push them away, far away, so that they would not trample or intrude on one's privacy, infecting the very air one breathed. Unimaginable, the extent to which such a situation can change a person into a hating creature with criminal thoughts—to feel day by day the threat, the attack, and the destruction of one's privacy. A room, separate if possible, with no neighbors, that was the dream of Madame Michel. Or a shack in the country with its own bit of garden, surrounded by silence, the silence of God's peace. And through open windows fresh air for Daniel and flowers all around. Then, oh, then, she would ask forgiveness from Michel's mother for having so desperately desired her death. Then she would ask God's forgiveness for having thrown the crucifix into the ash can, for having blasphemed, for having cursed providence—providence, who cares nothing for the poor.

And one evening the dream could no longer protect her. She went into a fit of trembling, began to cry, to scream, and to break the always-closed, imprisoning windows of the room. Finally she was subdued and taken away to St. Anne's.

So in the office at Emmaus the young workman, sunk in the old armchair, sobbed. The priest had seen men weep before, but these tears came from so deep an anguish that they haunted him for a long time after.

"Maybe it won't be so bad," Abbé Pierre said. "A nervous breakdown. She won't be in St. Anne's long. When she gets out, bring her here, we'll get her settled. There are little rooms on the second floor. And later, when the building is finished, we'll see."

The priest thought, "This is just an isolated case." He could not have guessed then where the road he had taken was to lead him.

It was in the Vincennes bus that Madame L. heard talk of a priest who had adopted two families and who was building homes.

She, too, told her story, huddled in the old office armchair. She, her husband, and three children had gone to French West Africa armed with hope and a contract for a job in forest development. On leaving they had sold their furniture, believing in the company promise that they would make their stake out there. They arrived. The two younger children became sick and one died of dysentery. Then the mother, anxious for the two others, packed up and returned to France. Her husband, however, remained to work for a few years more and every summer returned home to the city where she had settled in a hotel. Then, for three whole months, she got no news, and no money arrived. She wrote. No reply. Now, recently, a letter from the company had come telling her that her husband was sick and could not be moved for the moment. Unable to pay for her room, she had been sleeping with her two children in a garage in Neuilly-sur-Marne. The owner rented her a corner for 3,000 francs a month.

"But this can't go on any longer—the place is an icebox. We sleep on cold cement. My child is sick, and I must get a place. Father, you can find me shelter. I know you have helped two families. Find a roof to put over our heads, too."

"Oh, my God," thought the priest. "This logic based on confidence. It's true, I have helped two families, and there is no real reason why I should not continue. But how? This they never ask themselves. They just believe . . ."

And so the procession continued and grew: homeless families flocking eagerly about the priest and Emmaus. The inexorable demand sapped the strength, robbed the time and the resources of this man who could not let down the trust of these unfortunate people.

And unbelievable were the secret confidences that the walls

of the little office at Emmaus heard from all these desperate human beings, persons who for the first time felt they were being listened to.

"We're not living like humans any more, Monsieur l'Abbé." A woman of forty-five years who looked sixty spoke. Mother and housewife, she was relating the horror of life with old and young packed together into a slum, sleeping on mattresses and even on the ground.

"Not like humans, Monsieur l'Abbé. Like animals. My little Nicole, she's my youngest—only fifteen . . ."

She broke down. How can she go on, carrying this great shame? The poor have only their dignity. But dignity is impossible to keep, when conditions of life become inhuman.

". . . that lovely girl . . . and now she's pregnant."

Hiding her face, the mother shudders and sobs. "Pregnant, because of everyone sleeping together."

His heart wrung with pity, the priest added this case history to his files. It was not poor Nicole he accused, nor the father, nor the brother, but society. It was the result of legislators unable to cope with the problem, of the blindness and the selfishness of individuals.

In the region of Paris 200,000 poor, more than 6,000 of them children, were packed into hotels, furnished rooms, unsanitary slums with bad air and poor sleeping conditions. In Montreuil 10,000 homeless people every night looked for a chance shelter. Fifteen thousand lived in hotels giving half or more of their pay for a room where they could neither cook a meal nor wash their clothes. In France alone there were 7,000,000 poorly housed people.

This terrifying scandal, this shortage of housing for the poor which would stir up public opinion and the inertia of public authorities only several years later, Abbé Pierre learned at first-hand during that summer as more and more of these families begged him for shelter at Emmaus.

"How can people remain unaware of this? Why isn't something being done?" the Father kept repeating to himself. For him the revelation was stupefying. But soon he became a specialist. There were more than just a few isolated cases. Laden with their suitcases, their cardboard boxes, their perambulators, they were now legion, these derelicts of eternal chaos, this re-treating army of women and children whose eyes were the eyes of hunted animals, of young fathers whose faces were white and strained with despair.

"We're fed up; we just can't take any more." (And the walls echoed their despair: "So what? Go on, keep looking.")

During the war the misfortune of uprooting, of wandering in the rain, of nights outdoors affected all the nation, rich and poor alike. But for hundreds of thousands the flight did not stop with the return of peace. This almost invisible tide of "refugees" for-ever without refuge simply ceased to concern anyone. Instead, people were fearful. Those who felt they were protecting their own homes were irritated. In Paris alone, especially in wealthy districts, how many empty or half-occupied apartments would have been available had their proprietors not preferred to pay taxes rather than accept an unfortunate family? Or how many maids' rooms might have sheltered these wandering ones had not the owners been reluctant to meet on the stairs people less respectable looking than themselves? How many crimes were committed simply because doors were closed against these home-less? Later people would say: "I didn't know." Because of that, and *particularly* because of that, we shall be taken to account.

There was no law insuring shelter for those who own nothing in the world except a suitcase and a baby; there were only laws forbidding vagrancy. Poorhouses, prisons, hospitals, common graves were overpopulated. Law courts were overrun with cases of the poor driven to crime because of their lot.

The material ruins of war had been cleared away, but the ruin of society went on, created by a sub-proletariat of homeless, of young married couples whose homes had been destroyed by hate, divorce, alcohol, sickness, whose children were abandoned in the street. This was a generation condemned to death—to a slow and brutal death.

8: *Djibouti Meets Noëlle*

AUTUMN. The construction team had returned to Emmaus, The inn was empty of visiting youths. Only the Saturday groups still came to liven up the corner known as "Clos Fleuri." Over at La Barrière, in the large house and in the three bungalows, eight families were sheltered from the winter cold. Eight families. Fourteen children saved, but here at Emmaus the endless procession continued.

Djibouti, with some planks, had built a machinery and carpenter's workshop against the right wing of the house. Here he arranged a corner for himself, where he slept. He preferred solitude. New boarders had increased the permanent group lodged in the basement, but in this shed Djibouti was on his own. And he did have company. He had brought Finaud with him from the Barrière building lot, and he shared his soup with the puppy. While he was tinkering, the dog, sitting in a wooden box filled with shavings, watched him. The rain hammered down on the tin roof. Outside, the wind was blowing. Djibouti was happy to be working here alone with a roof over his head. There was always something to be done for the big house, and now they were preparing to enlarge one wing—the one he had built his shed against. He wouldn't be able to stay on much longer in this peaceful workshop.

These days the Father did not leave the large house so often as before, for the stream of visitors was incessant. From where Djibouti worked, he knew from the mere crunching of steps in the court, a certain sound of shoes on the gravel, and the sound of the wheels of a baby carriage, that another family had come to Abbé Pierre for help, shelter, or a job for the head of the family. Work meant a roof and a meal.

He could hear their voices, dull, timid, addressing Bastien or Étienne who were busy fixing up the kitchen in the bungalow to the left of the court.

"The Father? Is he there?"

This stream of jobless and homeless that occupied the time and drained the strength of Abbé Pierre irritated Djibouti. It meant unforeseen chores, but it was not so much the excess work that worried Djibouti as it was Abbé Pierre's despair at his own helplessness.

Sometimes after these visits the Father would come to the workshop, for he himself liked to tinker. His thin face was more drawn than ever. He would pass his hand over his brow and repeat: *"Mon Dieu, Mon Dieu,"* so tired, so tortured was he with the sorrows of others.

His heart overflowing with sympathy, Djibouti would have liked to say, "I am here, Father," but he didn't dare. And anyway what help would it have been? The best he could do was to work as hard as possible to lighten the Father's load. And not to disappoint him. It didn't matter to Djibouti whether the Father saw him working. Djibouti longed for him to understand his devotion.

But what upset Djibouti most of all was the courage with which Abbé Pierre controlled his despair. He would straighten his back, lift his head, and say: "Let's go finish fixing those corridor shelves on the second floor," and he would smile. Faced with this valiant smile, Djibouti would feel his own eyes filling with tears. "How can he keep on like this? How does he get so much strength from this exhaustion and feel such joy in spite of it all?"

One day the Father said to him: "What have you done to your eye?"

"Ran into a plank."

"Wise one."

The night before, the Kangaroo had been drinking again. This happened once or twice every month. Bastien drank, too. Was the Father aware of this? No doubt he was. But it was better to close one's eyes to some things. To have forbidden it would have done no good. But this time the Kangaroo had taken Étienne along. The kid had come back drunk. Djibouti could not take that, and had laid a heavy hand on the Kangaroo's shoulder.

"You dirty rat. So this is what you do with the Father's money? Him who's working his fingers to the bone for us?"

The Kangaroo landed a solid right on Djibouti.

Djibouti might have hit back. He wasn't afraid of the ex-boxer, who was reeling in front of him, but he held back and moved away. The Father must not hear of this.

A few days later the Kangaroo left Emmaus. The Saturday night before there had been young people at the inn. A girls' choir had come for the week-end. The Kangaroo had staggered in drunk, still carrying a liter of wine in his hand. By chance the Father happened to be in the court. Some of the young girls were passing only a few steps away.

"Hand me that bottle," said the Father under his breath.

It was the first time the Kangaroo had heard this voice filled with anger. Stunned, he held out the bottle. The Father turned away and poured the wine onto the ground.

Wine poured into a glass sparkles and sings. Spilt onto the gravel, it made a violet pool, hideous, a bubbling liquid mess that made one want to throw up.

"No, Father, please don't do that," stammered the Kangaroo, terrified as though he were witnessing a sacrilege. As the last drop fell to the ground, the Kangaroo turned round and in silence headed out through the gates in the direction of Paris.

The team grew by leaps and bounds. From every quarter more dispossessed comrades came to beg for a roof in the same way that Djibouti had before them. An ex-medic who had become a vagabond after serving ten years for practicing abortion; a divorced neurotic; an accountant out of a job; a one-legged youth; a young printer who, jobless and homeless, had been obliged to send his wife and child back to her parents.

Also two Indo-China veterans, like Baptiste. They were young volunteers, marked by combat and the cruel climate, one shaking with fever and nerves, the other disfigured by a grenade that had blown off his nose. There was an old deportee, too, back from the German death camps. Incapable of readjusting himself to a normal life, the hero of yesterday was now a wreck and wanted by no one. The Resistance? Such an old story today. . . .

How could one refuse to take them in?

One day the police telephoned the Father asking for details concerning one of the unfortunate men he had received.

"You are asking me, Monsieur le Commissaire, to help you arrest one of the men who have come to seek refuge with me? Let's be serious. To each his own role. Do I ask you to help me with confession?"

Nevertheless, hard as he might try to defend them, all Abbé Pierre could do was to offer a little work, a temporary refuge, but not at all that purpose, which would give them unity, force, a feeling of permanence.

One evening in October, sitting in the workshop, Djibouti saw the Father so desperate that he did not even offer a greeting. He caressed his dog in silence. Finally Djibouti ventured awkwardly:

"You are sad this evening, Father?"

The thin face relaxed, the dark eyes filled with warmth.

"Not sad, Djibouti. Just a little tired."

And then after a silence, perhaps less to his companion than to himself, he said in a low voice:

"This morning I had three visitors. What can I do? It's intolerable, this endless stream of people who have confidence in us. Such disappointments, such hopelessness. This afternoon I went out to Versailles. Coming back I passed through Vanves. There in an empty lot I discovered a family. Not vagabonds, not wastrels, but workmen, living under a tarpaulin. Once they had three children. Two did not live, and now a fourth is on its way. . . . I cannot even take them in. There's no room. But at all costs they must have shelter in time for the baby's birth."

"What we need is land, a house. We must build."

He stopped, thought for a minute, then smiled.

"It must work out—it always does work out."

"Yes," agreed Djibouti.

"You see Providence always takes care of us. Sometimes it comes fifteen minutes late so that we can grasp better the love the Lord has for us—and also the truth of our helplessness without Him."

"Yes," said Djibouti, not following at all.

"The love of the Lord for us." No, he could not understand that, on seeing the suffering of people. And the Father himself, up to his neck in the suffering of millions of innocent people, was still talking of God's love for us. . . . Djibouti simply could not understand. When the Father left, Djibouti tried rolling a cigarette. His hands shook. So that was it, that was Abbé Pierre's secret. This was the thing that permitted him to draw strength and joy from the depths of his fatigue and distress, never to be really desperate. It was God.

"As for me," murmured Djibouti, "I don't believe in miracles. I just believe in you, Father."

Two days later, on an icy cold morning, Djibouti met Noëlle for the first time. This was for him, after meeting Abbé Pierre, his second great adventure at Emmaus. A very personal adventure. He loved Abbé Pierre. To him Djibouti dedicated feelings that were stronger than any he had ever held for any other human being. But apart from this devotion, his concept of life was entirely self-centered. The misery of others left him cold, even sickened him. What was the use to waste one's strength in pity, to go to pieces over a child, especially someone else's child? That was sheer luxury, useless and false. Help—that's all they needed.

But on this particular day he was installing a stove in one of the small bungalows. This had been the chapel site. "Now," as Abbé Pierre said, "that the *Bon Dieu* has found shelter in the back of the park," and now that Raoul and his family had moved to La Barrière into their own bungalow, the pavilion stood empty. It had been decided that the men who were living in the basement would move there.

Standing on the stove, Djibouti and Alexandre, an ex-wool salesman, were putting the pipe through a ventilator. Through the mist he saw a little girl, a child of about two or three, dressed in a coat cut from old military cloth. She was walking out of the yard toward the gate, treading the iced pathway with a small, firm step.

For a moment, not moving, Djibouti watched the little figure, then he shrugged.

"So what, and where's her mother anyway?"

But down by the road he could hear the roar of an approaching truck. He was about to take up his work again but, fascinated, he continued to watch the child as he could hear, louder now, the noise of the oncoming vehicle. Letting go the stovepipe, he gingerly stepped down from his perch, went limping into the courtyard, and then started to run. The child had gone out the gate and stepped off the pavement. The huge truck honked, once, twice, and the child stopped short right in the middle of the road. As the heavy truck jammed on its brakes and skidded down the icy road toward the still figure, Djibouti leaped. With the hood only two yards away he seized the child by her collar and dragged her to the side of the road.

"Can't you keep an eye on your kid, you louse?" yelled the driver, shifting gears to start off again.

Djibouti didn't hear.

"Why, you little . . ." he stammered, shaking the child. "What in the world . . . ?"

He was trembling with rage and his hand itched to slap her face. But the child looked up at him without a trace of fear. She gazed at him with her great dark eyes and smiled.

"My mummie . . ." she started to say.

"Yes, come on," said Djibouti. He took her hand and they crossed the street.

"Noëlle!" shouted a woman's voice from the porch.

"Mama!" answered the child.

Djibouti let her run toward her mother. The young woman was pregnant; her face was the color of earth.

"Better keep an eye on the kid," Djibouti growled.

"I told her not to leave the bottom steps," said Madame Vatier, "but while I was talking to the lady in the office . . ."

"I'm hungry," said little Noëlle.

"We've been waiting for the Father almost two hours," the mother explained.

"Come into the kitchen," said Djibouti. "I'll heat something up for you."

And unwittingly he stretched out his hand to the child, who took it and went with him.

Suddenly it occurred to him that this little girl had the same color hair and was about the same age as the child he had killed with his truck on that road near Étampes. . . .

"For the coming winter, I can promise," said Abbé Pierre to the Vatiers, "you will be living in a house."

✳ II ✳

THE RAGPICKER BUILDERS

9: *Clos Fleuri*
"Operation Corn Turnip"

F ROM that day on Abbé Pierre received many visitors at Emmaus; but following these interviews he did not appear to Djibouti to be as depressed as formerly. Djibouti had noted, without attaching importance to it, that instead of receiving these visitors singly, he called them in in groups. Frequently he would leave, taking a group of them with him in his rickety truck.

One evening the priest announced that he had bought more land, a much larger piece than the Barrière lot. It was but half an hour's walk from Emmaus. He added that he was working on development plans with a group of potential landowners.

"For more building?"

"Yes."

The priest worked rapidly. Four days later, in mid-October, he asked Djibouti and three others to go with him to see the new lot.

On the way over in the old car he told them the story. He just had to do something, he said, particularly after having discovered the family with the little girl living under the tarpaulin, and another child on the way. He had discussed some ideas with a group of workers, including the family under the canvas, and they had made up their minds at once to form a corporation. They had no money but that was not going to stop them. A real-estate agent made an offer of land. It would take them ten years to pay for it on the installment plan, but the plot was over 8,000 yards square. Engineers had gone to work at once tracing a road across the plot and drawing plans for twenty gardens, measuring about 350 square yards.

"But the building materials, Father?" one of the team queried.

"I have parts of the military barracks I bought at Aubervilliers and at St.-Ouen. Then we have made a contract with a demolition contractor who lets us have boards and stones at a good price. We can build small bungalows of two and three rooms. I am asking you to give the men a hand here just as you did at La Barrière. First clear the wasteland and then build."

"Naturally, we will," said the men in the team.

"We will call this land Clos Fleuri, and we will grow houses, children, and flowers."

"Clos Fleuri"—Djibouti liked the sound of this name. In the drizzle of this October morning he dreamed of a corner in the open country in springtime. There was an orchard filled with long grass; gold buttercups and white daisies swayed in the breeze under the apple blossoms and flowering peach trees. The car would leave the national highway, turn into a lane running along the railway embankment. On the left were the gasworks. A few trees in a field of dry stalks of corn and turnips. This was the future Clos Fleuri, a piece of land for cultivation. It was a no-man's land between town and the real country, already threatened by the invasion of civilization.

Two men, future landowners, were already on the spot. Three more arrived on bicycles. Soon after a car brought to the spot the owner of the land. All morning, in the rain, the priest walked up, down, and across his new acquisition. Water in hand, he referred to his plan. Trotting behind him, in the slimy mud, Djibouti stretched the string and planted pickets along the future road. Then they tagged and numbered the lots.

Around noon the Father left for Emmaus, and all the men adjourned to the café on the edge of the national highway. There the Emmaus team "met" the five or six future proprietors. They ate together and emptied a few bottles of wine. After the cheese, tongues were loosened.

"We live in two rooms," said Jules, a thin, pale-faced boy of seventeen. "Two rooms near the Porte St. Martin. Luxury, huh? But listen . . ."

His laugh was bitter.

"There are seventeen of us in those two rooms. Eleven kids, counting myself. My brother's two sons are dead. One of my sister's boys is in a reform school. One of her little girls has rickets and is getting tuberculosis. My kid brother heard someone mention the Father. That's why I'm here. I have some free time because of the strike."

And so it went. Each of these men had lived one or another episode of the same monotonous story—overcrowded slums, overpriced hotels, the streets, divorce, sickness, alcohol, death, occasionally even a sister who became a prostitute, a younger brother who disappeared from the neighborhood to end in a reform school. They spoke of all this simply, without dramatics, knowing the others would understand, united as they were in the same misery and from now on in the same new hope.

"Legally, when you're dead you've a right to a better place than when you're living," one of them concluded. "This is the truth that I'm going to tell you. When my granddad decided to buy a family vault in the cemetery, the city gave him the compulsory measurements for six caskets. Thirty-three feet by ten. Near where I live I know three families. There are nine people, counting the babies, and they live in one room measuring thirty-three by ten. There isn't room for a table or a slop pail. You have to move the babies' boxes to open the door. They went to the city welfare board and the Red Cross; they went to see their deputies. Nothing for them. They'll have to wait for the undertakers to get living space."

The rain had stopped. The meal over, the last cigarette smoked, the men were impatient to get back to the plot of ground which they already alluded to as "their" lot. The first thing to be done was to clear out the turnips, corn, and weeds.

"Need any help?" Djibouti asked young Jules. "That's what we're here for."

The latter, legs spread, sleeves rolled up over his skinny arms, smiled as he contemplated his "lot." Fifty feet by about seventy with four stakes marking the boundaries. The sky above over his land was his, too. So the earth—as deep down as it went. And best of all, there was a little apple tree with several apples hanging from its branches. Having been one of the very first to come to terms with the priest, he was given the right to choose his own lot.

"No," said young Jules. "Not me, mister. I'm not going to let anyone work my corner. It's gonna all be done by me."

So Djibouti attacked a plot of land right at the end of the cornfield where no one was working. It touched the main road, reached up the slope.

He pulled out the dry cornstalks. They tore at his hands but he soon piled them up and struck a match to the heap. The bonfire made a great billow of smoke. . . .

In the middle of the afternoon the Father returned. He brought with him two tents, and he immediately left again to bring some straw. Later a truck appeared, towing a gypsy wagon onto the lot. Inside was the Spanish woman who made coffee for the men on her spirit lamp.

About six o'clock the lights went on in the dark mass of the gasworks. In the dusk Djibouti saw a man approaching on a bicycle. He stopped, got down, and pulled out a piece of paper which he studied.

"Am I wrong?" he said. "Isn't this my lot Number 1? The Father marked it down on a piece of paper for me."

"Could be," said Djibouti.

"But I see you working here."

"I'm not the owner," said Djibouti. "I'm just doing this for the Father."

"For me, then, you mean," said the man, smiling.

He put down his bike.

"You've done me a great favor," he said.

Together they finished work in the dusk. The stars were bright in the clear, cold sky. The massive silhouette of the gasworks stood out against a backdrop of blinking lights and the distant glow of the city. From the top of the embankment one of the big railroad signal beacons threw a faint light on their field.

By eight o'clock they had finished. The other men were now leaving for Emmaus.

The man said: "Have a drink?"

"No," answered Djibouti. "See you tomorrow."

"*Salut.* So long. My name is Marcel. Marcel Vatier. I'm off to Vanves. It's quite a way. See you tomorrow."

Remaining alone, Djibouti gave the strange encampment the once-over. The tents and the gypsy wagon showed through the pungent bonfire smoke that trailed close to the ground. Here and there heaps of cornstalks were still smouldering. In one of the conical tents, lighted by a storm lamp, a family ate their meal seated in a circle on the straw. For tomorrow, the priest had promised beds. The woman in the wagon was cooking for a neighbor family. Only young Jules, determined and happy, was still at work pulling out turnips from under his tree.

The stars in the icy sky, the whistle of a train, the huge silhouette of the factory, the little light of the petrol lamp seen through the smoke of the bonfires, and the figure of the boy Jules still at work in the dusk—these voices, these lives that in this desolate wilderness were taking possession of their property—all this was to Djibouti a "sign," and he seemed to hear an appeal. And just as at certain hours in the past summer, under the little poplar tree at Barrière, he felt strangely moved and more hungry for solitude than ever. Not because he was sad, but because he felt a kind of kinship toward all this, toward people, life, and himself—a sort of reconciliation after a very long and hate-filled quarrel. He wanted to enjoy this feeling in peace. He started out on foot to Emmaus, limping badly. After so much bending down in the field his back ached, too. But the pain in no way interfered with his contentment.

Next morning Djibouti left Emmaus early for Clos Fleuri. The day was going to be fine. Arriving at the lot, he saw a truck stopped at the corner where they had been clearing the night before. Marcel Vatier was unloading rafters and planks with the aid of the driver.

"*Salut,*" said Vatier, passing him a plank before he even had time to take off his coat.

Young Jules nodded to him from across the field. Somewhere he had scrounged a wheelbarrow which he was filling with stones that he picked off the slope. These he then emptied on his lot. The kids from one of the family tents were running to the fountain near the road, calling the children in the next tent as they went by: "Lucien, Jacqueline." The tent was closed, but the little chimney that poked through a crack in the door was smoking. A young woman wearing a blue wrapper came out, looked at the surrounding countryside, and, smiling, passed her hand through her still-unbrushed hair. The sun glistened on the frost-crested furrows. Shining cobwebs caught at the grass and bushes bordering the road. The pale sunshine and crisp, fresh air were like a tonic which on this autumn morning awakened the women and children to their first day of liberty. It was truly the dawn of a new life. The truck pulled out. Marcel Vatier uncorked his thermos bottle, offered a cup of steaming coffee to Djibouti. They sipped at it alternately, sharing the same mug. Vatier said: "We discussed it at great length with the architect and the Father. I picked the two-room model, twenty-seven feet by ten."

He unfolded the blueprint.

"Ten feet for the bedroom. The dining-room-kitchen, seventeen. There are double walls of wood and the base is stone. Later it will all be made of stone."

"Yeh," said Djibouti. "That's how we built them on the lot at Barrière."

"Fine. Then you know the tune. The base takes longest, but the stones and cement should be here this morning. For the time being we can always start the trench. To my way of thinking we should leave five meters of garden in the front."

Smiling, he unfolded his yardstick. With stones and then stakes he marked the corners of his future home.

"Go and ask your buddy by the tree there where he found his wheelbarrow."

Jules hadn't really "knocked himself out," he said. He'd just borrowed it from an owner near the factory.

Just as Djibouti was about to leave the lot in quest of pickax and shovel he saw the approaching Mona, Abbé Pierre's precious truck. Here was the Father with a load of tools, blankets, and camp beds.

"How goes it, Djibouti? Are you helping Vatier?"

When the factory siren sounded at noon, they had finished digging the trench, but the truck with the stones and cement hadn't yet arrived.

"I'd better be getting along," said Vatier. "My wife wasn't too well this morning. She's expecting. I don't want her to have the baby under the tarpaulin."

Until that moment Djibouti hadn't realized that the family the Father had mentioned as living under a tarpaulin was, in fact, that of his friend.

"Your kid will be born here," he said.

"In that case, we'll have to make it snappy. I'll be seeing you. Maybe tonight, or tomorrow."

Djibouti took up his digging. The Mona went by again.

"Coming to eat at Emmaus with me?" said the Father.

"No, I'd better stick right here."

The Father handed him a piece of paper money.

"No, thanks. I have some cash on me. I'll get something at the café. What worries me is that the truck with the stones and cement isn't here yet."

"I'll give the contractor a call."

He stepped on the starter. Then his face appeared at the window again.

"And thanks."

He smiled, and his friendly look, expressing respect, trust, and friendship, stayed with Djibouti for a moment.

Merci. Thanks. How well he knew the value of the simplest words. The car started off. Djibouti pensively picked up his pickax.

"Thanks," repeated Djibouti to himself. Why had the Father thanked him? What have I ever done that's so special? He shouldn't be thanking me. He owes me nothing.

For a minute he tried to remember the favor he might have rendered the Father during the day, a special service that might have called for these thanks. There was nothing he could think of. All day long he'd been working on the lot. It could not be because of this work. Of course it is for him that I'm doing this chore. For Vatier, sure, but mainly for the Father. But if I was not doing this, what else could I be doing? I'd surely be dragging my feet someplace if I weren't working here. So it shouldn't be the Father thanking me. . . .

The more he thought of it, the stranger the word sounded. *Merci*—that hideous, smug little word. Dry and slimy at the same time. The servile and the worldly have it on their lips all the time. Their cut-rate thanks don't mean a thing. If this word loses its meaning, human relations become hypocritical and futile. . . .

Yet the word was solemn. Joyously solemn. Thanks. . . . I freely accept my engagement, I recognize my debt as a man who can honor it.

No, the Father shouldn't be thanking me. But was it for this reason alone that Djibouti should one day express the true, the overwhelming gratitude which was filling his heart? All this remained confused in his mind. But as a man he felt it. He was very thankful to the Father for having made of him the man he was today, standing in this field, on this lot—free.

10: *First Birth at Clos Fleuri*

THE first two buildings to be finished at Clos Fleuri were a tool cabin and the Vatiers' little house. This took ten days. When the base walls were finished, the wood panels took practically no time at all. Djibouti was on the job from morning till night with Baptiste, two other companions from Emmaus, and a man from the building contractors. Each of them shared the Father's anxiety in getting the house built before Madame Vatier gave birth to the baby. It was a race with life. Marcel came over on his bicycle after working hours at the factory, and stayed until late into the night. Luckily the weather remained good and work was going on all over the lot. Young Jules brought a daily load of material and furniture in a pushcart all the way from Paris. Enclosures were being put up and new tents pitched. A new family with five children had moved in. They arrived in a remnant of an old bus that the Father had purchased from the city. Three Companions of Emmaus were leveling the street and putting down gravel. The electricians were already putting up poles. Soon there would be a line to the gasworks and another to the rail terminal. Clos Fleuri was no longer a vacant lot. It had become a building lot and would soon bear the name of "city."

"How in the world does he manage, the Father?" thought Djibouti to himself. "He always seems to find a way to raise money."

He was aware that some of these people had been able to pay

in installments for the land and building; but the Father was
constantly looking for more funds, borrowing always to solve a
problem, taking new steps, and getting more deeply involved all
the time. Djibouti had the feeling that no one in Clos Fleuri or
at Emmaus had the slightest idea of the enormous task, the
thousand-and-one responsibilities which the organizer was continually tackling. The families depended on him, appealed to
him for everything: a stove, fresh straw, wood for heating, water,
a cradle for the baby.

"We'll mention it to the Father. We'll ask the Father. The
Father will know. He'll find it . . ."

This childish confidence which further loaded down the
priest's stooping shoulders annoyed Djibouti beyond words. The
Father, after all, could not work miracles. Miracles don't exist;
unless you call simple goodness in action a miracle.

The Father remained unperturbed, jotted down memos,
stroked the children's heads, went flying off in his old car. He
returned with beds, pots and pans, chairs, toys, and a new family
to shelter.

On a warm Thursday morning Vatier arrived on the lot with
little Noëlle on the baggage rack of his bicycle.

"Listen," he said to Djibouti. "My wife isn't well. Would you
mind keeping an eye on the kid for the day? I'll pick her up this
evening."

"We've met already," growled Djibouti. "We saw each other
at Emmaus."

He recognized the child as the one who had almost been
crushed under the wheels of that truck. Marcel left a small
package containing the child's lunch and a thermos bottle filled
with hot milk.

"This is Uncle Djibouti," he said to the little girl. "And you
are going to be a good girl and stay here with him all day. Say
hello."

Djibouti stretched out his hand.

"No," said the child, and clutching at her father's legs, she
kissed him as he bent over her.

"She's pretty wild and does as she likes. By-by, cutie pie," said
the father.

As he left, the little girl stood motionless and large tears ran down her cheeks.

"Now what's all this?" said Djibouti, at a loss as to what he might do to comfort her. "He'll be back, your daddy."

He undid the parcel and handed her a piece of chocolate.

"Want some milk?"

"No," said the little girl, taking the chocolate.

It took the dog, Finaud, to cheer her up. He had come to the lot in the morning with his master. He had been doing the rounds of the "city." First he had visited the little bitch who slept between the wheels of the gypsy wagon in a barrel. Then he returned to lot Number 1 and with his funny eyes, set under bushy brows, he watched his master sawing, hammering, and placing planks. Then he ran off again. He came to make friends with the little girl and put his head between her hands. Together they played for half an hour at the foot of the slope, then they both went to play with a little boy at the other tent on lot Number 7. Djibouti watched them from the corner of his eye. He saw the young woman in the blue wrapper bend down to speak to Noëlle. The little girl pointed toward Djibouti.

"Yes, she's mine, that little piece," he called, laughing.

"I'll take care of her for you," answered the woman.

At noon Djibouti ate under the tent with the woman, her little boy, and Noëlle.

"It was in the subway, three weeks ago, that I first met the Father," confided Lucie Marchand.

On that evening at about eight o'clock, gazing from the door of a subway train, the Father had noticed a young woman with a little boy of three or four sitting on a platform bench. Everyone sees this every day without taking the slightest notice, without stopping to think that a subway station is not a railroad waiting room. Those who remain sitting when the train gets in, what are they waiting for? A date? Hardly. If they are not traveling, it means they have nowhere else to go. It means that this seat on the subway platform is their only refuge, for it's raining outside and there's no more money. The tens of thousands of people who pass to and fro daily never think about this. One hardly notices these human derelicts. In a bustling city it's seldom that a man stops to think about his fellow man. But that evening at six o'clock the Father saw the same woman and child seated in the same place. He left the train to go up and speak to her.

For an entire month Madame Marchand and her little boy had been living without a fixed home. Her husband, a printer, was in a sanatorium. She had no skilled training. She came from a small bourgeois family and had lived with her parents in the north of France until her marriage. Dressmaking, household chores, or bookkeeping—she would take any sort of work.

Up to the present the want ads had offered nothing. She had no references, no certificates, and then this handicap, the child. However, in last evening's paper she had finally seen an ad. A furniture manufacturer was looking for a servant to live in. He lived near the Place de la Nation. It was because she had an appointment with him next morning early that she was waiting here. When the metro gates closed she would walk the streets. She still had some hope, when she told Abbé Pierre her story. But in case of failure, the latter gave her the address of Emmaus.

Ten days later the mail brought him a letter:

"Twice already, Monsieur M, my new employer, has tried to break into my room when he was drunk. I cannot stay here any longer. You allowed me to hope you would find a refuge for me in your House. I beg you, answer me by return mail."

The Father answered: "Come."

Since then Abbé Pierre had found several scrubwoman jobs and some washing for her to do in the Emmaus neighborhood, and he had advanced her some money to insert a want ad. As to the lot and her future house, she had not wanted to become involved in a loan. The Father offered her free temporary shelter.

"When my husband returns in good health, maybe we can afford to buy land for ourselves."

She related all this to Djibouti with the simplicity born of truth. And, for the "Bear," this was the first time in years that he had found himself with a young woman. A misogynist through experience, Djibouti suddenly saw the courage and fidelity of a woman struggling alone. Here she was, tranquil, dignified, and courageously gay. . . .

If only his own wife had wanted to wait for his return as
Madame Marchand was waiting for her husband. There was
his picture on the wall of the tent.

He emptied his cup of coffee and rose from the wooden crate
on which he had been sitting.

"I'm going back to work."

Two Companions of Emmaus, fifty meters from Madame
Marchand's tent, were leveling the "road" with sledge hammers,
their bare torsos glistening in the heat. One of them stopped,
looked toward the tent, smiled. He was a husky, good-looking
youth, dark, and with a small mustache.

"Who's he?" said Lucie Marchand, frowning.

"A newcomer to Emmaus. They call him Louis. That's all I
know."

"Yesterday he called on me twice. I don't like him."

"Listen, if he ever . . ." growled Djibouti.

She laughed. "I'm big enough to take care of myself. By-by,
I'll keep the little girl."

That evening, as the priest was taking the men back to Emmaus, he made a detour and stopped his car at a hardware store.
He bought a pot of paint and a brush and said to Djibouti:

"I would like you to make me a panel this evening. It must
measure forty by twelve inches."

In his workshop Djibouti sawed, planed, and put the panel
together. The Father opened the pot of paint, and in graceful
green letters printed the words:

CAMPERS' ASSOCIATION

"We will hang this at the entrance to Clos Fleuri."

Djibouti frowned. He didn't get it at all. The joke annoyed
him.

"Campers' Association?"

"Sure. You see, we're building illegally. We're on unzoned
land. We have no building permit. I'd rather have written,
PERMIT TO LIVE on this board, behind which twenty families
can eventually build in peace, and behind which the Vatier
baby will be born in peace, too."

The Vatier family was to have moved in at 7 P.M. Saturday evening. It was the week of All Saints. As dusk fell, the roof was not yet finished and the men worked feverishly in the chilly wind. The Father had parked his truck on the road along the embankment and had turned the headlights full on the house. Perched on the pinnacle of the rafters, he was nailing down the sheets of tin.

At six-thirty young Antoine, another newcomer to Emmaus, arrived on his bicycle.

"Father, Mademoiselle has sent me to tell you not to forget the time your plane leaves."

"Yes," said the Father; "just five minutes more."

As president of the executive committee of a World Federalist movement, Abbé Pierre was supposed to open that very evening in London, at the side of Lord Beveridge, a parliamentary congress.

"We must finish this roof," he said, "because if it's not done right the authorities will fuss and may forbid the moving in during my absence."

"Just let them try it," said one of the men. "But hurry, Father, it's six-thirty."

"I'm coming right away."

He hammered in a last nail, climbed down the ladder.

"Luckily my clean cassock is in the car," he said. "I can wash my hands on the plane."

He jumped into his car and went off with a roar.

At Le Bourget airport the plane's propellers were spinning. Abbé Pierre raced up the gangway and the plane took off immediately.

Two hours later, at Church House, before representatives of twenty-two nations, he gave the inaugural speech that started with these words:

"The man addressing you is no longer a parliamentary delegate but one of a community of miserable people."

This introduction made a profound impression. His new title of "delegate of misery" conferred on him possibly a greater authority than that of an acting parliamentarian.

Old Lord Beveridge, at the moment of Abbé Pierre's imminent re-election as president, pronounced the following words:

"I am voting for the Abbé because he speaks a French that every man can understand."

Three days later, on Tuesday night, the Vatiers moved. Marcel rapped on the gypsy-wagon door. The Spanish woman got up and awakened Madame Marchand. At one o'clock little Jeanne was born, in a warm, clean house—a lovely baby who wanted just one thing, to live.

The Father heard the news on his return from London.

"The first baby at Clos Fleuri," he murmured. "She owes her life to the Companions of Emmaus."

11: *Difficulties with the Authorities*

T HOUGH born in her own home, little Jeanne's arrival into this world was illegitimate. She could have been born and died out in the open, and that would have been perfectly legal. But she was born and was growing up in the security of a home which by law the priest had not even had the right to build.

"You should have known this, Monsieur l'Abbé."

The state official who had summoned Abbé Pierre to his office was aware of the priest's activities. He spoke clearly, with the authority of a man who knew his subject. The priest watched him, listened to him, and remained silent. Between the two men, there on the desk, lay the thick file entitled "Clos Fleuri." It had become the symbolic wall which too frequently separates law and order from charity.

The visitor's silence, his calm attitude, both troubled and annoyed the official. It seemed like a challenge. Sharply tapping the file, he repeated that "he knew perfectly well all that was going on at Clos Fleuri." He knew. "Now come along; all is not lost." He knew, and the priest must understand. There was a further silence, then the little word rang out like a pistol shot.

"A zone. We have finally demolished this zone. It was no easy task. It has taken us years to wipe out this blot. We cannot permit this gangrene once again to disfigure the access to the city. It always starts over again; when there are not ragpickers' tents, there are the sheds and hovels of this shanty town. . . . We know what has to be done in all this. . . . When the Minister of Reconstruction and City Planning is putting the final touch to a large-scale modern project, it is inadmissible to permit the construction of such primitive developments as yours. These shanties are built like primitive huts anyhow, without either a building permit or regulation utilities. . . ."

The priest rose to leave.

"Sir," he said, "I refuse to pursue a conversation based simply on two points: first, what *should* have been, according to official plans, and what, in the meantime, I have been able to provide for these families. I will only agree to listen if you will be realistic. By this I mean if you will consider these three premises: Number one, fine homes *should* have been planned; two, consider what we have given the families as an urgent measure; and third, think of the places in which they would continue to rot and die if we had not given them this. . . . This is what you have overlooked altogether."

The official fell silent in his turn and then, changing his tone, "I beg you, be seated, Monsieur l'Abbé. Let us discuss this."

Now it was the visitor who talked. First he spoke in his own defense. Then he became the prosecutor.

"We regret having had to build illegally. As an ex-parliamentarian I respect the law. Law is necessary. But there are certain urgent cases where the law of conscience, the natural law, overrules written law. You tell me you have abolished the zone. If I wanted to be harsh I could answer: You have not abolished the misery of the zone. You have concealed it, but it still exists. It has entered into Paris, into the overcrowded slums, into the attics, into unlivable cellars. Outside Paris, by broad daylight, the scandal was too apparent. In Paris, this scattered misery, dispersed and drowned in the crowd, is less noticeable. Your main complaint against us is that we have pulled the camouflage off the misery. I agree with you entirely that we have not been able to offer the most modern comfort to the poor we have sheltered, but let me show you from what impossible situations we have extricated some of them."

Now it was Abbé Pierre's turn to open his brief case. Pulling several cases from his files, he related to the official the case of Michel whose wife had lost her reason living with nine others in a room; the case of little Nicole, who, obliged because of cramped quarters to share a straw mattress with her brothers, became pregnant; the case of Madame N. and her children whose only refuge was a garage corner; that of Madame Marchand, that of the Vatiers who lived for months under a tarpaulin. Should one wait still longer and renounce sheltering them from winter?

To put in water mains, electric lines, and sewage systems would have taken 350,000 francs per family, at least, and a six months' delay, maybe more. Winter months—six mortal months. Where is the offense? Where is one's duty? Should one respect life or the law?

"It's because we're poor," concluded the priest, "that we were obliged to overlook the permit. This we couldn't help. We practiced the opposite of what is required by law because our order of doing things puts life before law. This seemed a natural order, considering the state of desperate urgency. Little by little we will install electricity, water mains, and septic tanks. And if we're asked, 'Where are your building permits?' we will answer, 'We are too poor to obtain them at once.' But all these families were not too poor to be born. If you demand our papers, we will put up all the birth records of the children born at Clos Fleuri on a bulletin board which will say 'Permit to Live.' And we will invite the press, the radio, and newsreels to see the display."

"Now, now, keep calm, Monsieur l'Abbé. We are not demanding the death of the sinner."

At the office door, the official held out his hand.

"Our department will not take any action against you. But it might be wise for you to be covered by a ministerial authorization."

The priest knew one of the chiefs of the Cabinet quite well. Though not close friends, the two men had mutual respect for each other despite their different temperaments. One was cold, slightly standoffish, impressed by his own importance. He created plans but was handicapped by administrative impotency, by legal restrictions he did not dare override.

The other all fire, the crusader of active idealism, not afraid of tearing off at any cost the mask of injustice, of cruelty, of aberrations tolerated by society; nor of bringing to these problems solutions that were often labeled anarchistic.

"Of course I'm not an anarchist," the priest repeated time and time again. "You know perfectly well that I have every respect for the law. I agree that your planning is essential, that city developments should impose reasonable limits, but that is only feasible over a long period. In the meantime, babies are dying."

His friend was silently staring at Abbé Pierre's hands. They had become hardened and torn with work on stone, wood, and iron. They were now the hands of a workman. His hands . . . and that voice; they were so convincing.

"Let me tell you this, too," said the priest. "You are carrying out perfectly exactly half of your work."

"What? I don't get you."

"It's this. If you are going to establish and put into action long-term programs, you should have thought of an emergency program to bridge the gap. One day the survivors of today's misery will doubtless live in your houses with automatic elevators. In the meantime, many are dying outside. I offer them my huts."

"You must understand that it is quite impossible for us to give special privileges, particularly to you, an ex-deputy. Why the Ministry risks questioning by Parliament . . ."

"Rest assured I am not asking you to break the law. I am not even asking you to modify the law. I do ask, however, that in certain emergency cases the law be deferred and softened; that exceptions be granted with the possibility of eventually achieving legal status."

The Cabinet chief hesitated and reflected quietly for a moment.

"An experiment—why not? I will speak to the Minister."

"Come and visit us, but be careful. I might put you to work."

But the priest did not win his cause so easily as that. He left without having obtained a promise. Months went by. Debts accumulated. Abbé Pierre's case was getting graver because new building was going on at Clos Fleuri. It was a year later when at last a circular reached the Administration delegates indicating the limitations (these were quickly accepted by the Father) within which the law would tolerate his daring plan. He would be allowed to finish the buildings under construction, but there was a clause forbidding new lots of the same type to be opened.

When the priest began welcoming and sheltering the homeless, he had hoped that he would be understood and helped. He lost his illusions very soon. Though he could understand how administrative red tape led to the inertia of certain social services, he was plunged into despair by the incomprehension of private individuals, the accusations inspired by selfishness and simple stupidity. But he never lost courage. The pain he felt, he simply added onto his other troubles. That autumn and winter of '51 were for Emmaus a period so difficult that later they were always alluded to as the "heroic period."

One day a left-wing doctrinary said to him, "You're a socialist without doubt, Monsieur l'Abbé, but you see what you are trying to do at Clos Fleuri we do not approve of."

"Why?"

"You only see the immediate. We see the over-all picture, the revolution in its sum total. You are replastering a rotten edifice that should be destroyed at its base. It's not through isolated individual solutions that you will ever come to a result. It is only by attacking the whole social and political structure. I can also tell you that you are being accused of having created Emmaus for your own election campaign."

"You know that isn't true, that I created Emmaus for my own political gain. Must we sit idle and do nothing simply because fools talk nonsense?"

"But you are weakening the force of revolt of the proletariat."

"You know very well, my friend, that I am fighting with all my might for broad social reforms, for the necessary institutional changes that will wipe out the cause of so much misery. There are plenty of rightists who defend private charity merely to delay any reforms that might cut into their privileges. But you, at the other extreme, you cannot hope to begin social revolution by sitting with your arms crossed before the distress that is under your very noses, distress that is urgent. We are trying to act in both directions. On one hand we clamor for social reforms, on the other we take in all those unfortunates who come to us for help. This is the thing that makes us strong."

Still more depressing than the attitude of local and state authorities was that of the "old-guard" conservatives.

One day a woman arrived at Emmaus and asked for an interview with the priest. She was not a case who had come for assistance but one of the dignified society figures who called on the priest from time to time. Generally they brought him linen, clothing, or money for his boarders. The Father received her in his office.

"It appears that we are neighbors, Monsieur l'Abbé. I mean that I own a villa next to Clos Fleuri. Actually I don't live there because I have a house in Paris."

"Goodness," thought the priest, "she is going to offer the villa for rent, or maybe even place it at the disposal of several families for nothing!"

The lady continued.

"So this is what I have come to ask you. Has it occurred to you that, should I decide to sell my villa, its value, because of the close proximity of your hovels, will be practically nil? Have you given this a thought, Monsieur l'Abbé?"

"No, Madame, alas, I have not thought about that."

There was a silence.

"I have been told you are building without permission."

"That's right."

"But you can be sued."

The priest stood up and said softly: "We could wish for nothing better, Madame, than that they should bring us to court. Then with all our force we will shout out the atrocious truth that is concealed from the public, misunderstood by the authorities. We will shout it out so that everyone may hear it!"

The dowager beat a hasty retreat. She left murmuring, "Worker-priest. Communist. Anarchist."

She passed unseeing before a picture of the Father next to the Pope, taken during one of the four private audiences that the Sovereign Pontiff had graciously granted him.

12: *The Vocation of Charity*

"**W**ILL you accept my offer to work with you for six months? My Superior has authorized my coming to you before my ordination. I feel the deep need of this experience."

The Father slowly reread the letter he had just received from a young seminarist. How close he felt to this youth, how this reminded him of his own feelings when he, too, was a young seminary student.

The boy would have to undergo the same apprenticeship of total devotion to charity that he had undergone. He would have to restrain his enthusiasm and retain joy, to conquer disillusionment and reach the hard truth of love.

The man of mercy and justice has even less power to escape his calling than the artist, the musician, the ambitious or rich man. His passion feeds on that which he finds most constant in this world, that which is most varied and abundant, suffering and injustice. And this will never deceive him as love might deceive a lover. Evil is a sure thing. The man of mercy is profoundly aware of this, yet he will never cease refuting it.

This letter took him back twenty-five years. He remembered how after his visit to the Cité Rambaud with his father, he and some other young friends explored the suburbs of Lyon, coming to the aid of the many unfortunate people who were living under conditions as atrocious as those in Paris.

A sentence from a letter received at that time from his best friend expressed the solemn fervor of these two fifteen-year-old boys and often came back to his mind to give him courage: "Each of us does what he wants with his life. Some of us drag it in the mud. When this happens we see just how revolting life can become. We should profit by this lesson and make of our own lives something glorious."

At nineteen, during an illness, a book reaffirmed for him the vocation he should follow. It revealed through the words of St. Francis of Assisi those things that come to a man who decides to give up everything to follow the higher demands of the vocation of charity: the Christian paradox (He who seeks to win the world will lose it), the constant problem that life poses (What is it that troubles you?) and the "foolish" security (Seek ye first the kingdom of God . . . all these things shall be added to you).

How could young Henri, whose bourgeois family fortune represented security and was ample enough for countless charitable deeds, have not felt fear at first? But at nineteen he felt again the torment he had experienced as a child of twelve when the terrible obligations of charity unrolled before his eyes. And now, at this point, he felt he must give up everything, become a poor man himself, plunge into a solitary existence without recourse. Then, as if to help him make his choice, he was possessed of an inner flame and a deep feeling of courage in his conviction. It was a Divine voice—irrefutable, unshakable.

From the Riviera where he was convalescing he returned to Lyon and announced to his father that he would like to become a priest. The news came as a shock to his parents, for the father had great ambitions for his son. He expected him to step in one day as head of the family business, just as he himself had. However, they voiced their pride in his decision and gave him their blessing. Faced suddenly with the prospect of this all-consuming vocation they suffered, but they accepted the sacrifice.

Henri then asked his father for his inheritance before he entered the priesthood. He distributed it in one day between foundations, hospitals, and the poor of Lyon. Then he entered the Capuchin Convent of St. Francis. During his novitiate his father, who had suffered for many years, died. The eve of his death he murmured: "May I, without being a coward, ask to die?"

And, having provided generously for a poor family in his will he added: "My greatest happiness is the thought that my last deed will serve to improve the life of others."

After seven years, Henri was obliged to give up monastic life for reasons of health. For several months he served as a parish assistant. Then came war and service in the Alps and Alsace. Sick, he was evacuated to a hospital in the Southern Zone. It was there he learned that the Armistice had been signed with the Germans. The dying man in the bed next to him clutched his hand, sobbed, and repeated over and over again that it could neither be true nor final; that one must hope against all hope.

Demobilized, the priest returned to his diocese. At the time he had no political beliefs, feeling simply that those in the government must surely be resolved, above all, to save and serve France and the French.

On a night in July 1942 (four months before the occupation of the Southern Zone) there was a ring at his doorbell in the presbytery of the Cathedral. He got up and opened the door to find a crowd of people, some dressed only in night clothes, begging him to hide them. What was happening? He was told that the police were raiding houses, dragging Jews from their beds, taking them away as they found them. They were loading the men into one truck, the women into another, children and even newborn babies into still a third one. Later it was learned that the men were sent to the east to the gas chambers and extermination camps and the women to Germany to satisfy the lusts of the troops. The children were turned over to public homes where all their identities were destroyed.

Now some miraculous escapees of this manhunt had come to ring at his door. They had run not to Abbé Pierre personally but to the nearest priest, the man of God. "Save us." And for that night he gave them his room. Next day he found refuge for them in friends' homes, in girls' schools, and in convents. And they kept coming in increasing numbers. It was obvious to Abbé Pierre that Providence did not wish him to rest. He was faced with the terrifying privilege of saving hunted souls at the risk of his own life. Then began the struggle of accepting daily the risk of death.

"Yes, this was a blessing," he wrote later. "To suffer oneself makes one much more understanding of others' suffering. One must have the privilege, which later was given to me, to be numbered among those who know that though innocent, they are forbidden to live, and, still worse, that their death is desired."

A Polish student rang his doorbell. His nerves had given way. He came from the north where he was being hunted. His physical appearance and accent revealed his Jewish origin. To keep him from the Germans it would be necessary to set up a file of documents proving the naturalization of his family several generations back. The priest hid him in the attic of a woman of his parish. While they were working on the complicated process of forging pieces for his file—birth certificates, christening and military papers—the poor boy, incapable of keeping still, came daily to pull the rectory bell. The priest begged him to stay in the attic. They were working on his case. All would be ready in a very few days now. One day Abbé Pierre even ran into him on the street. The priest scolded him. The next day the boy did not appear.

The following morning everything was ready. The priest went to take him the papers insuring his life and liberty. He asked the landlady if he was home. She said she had not seen him leave the house so he should be there. They opened the attic door. He had hanged himself.

The priest had been unable to pull this man back from the brink of death. As a savior of men this failure continued to obsess him, and behind every desperate case that later presented itself at Emmaus he seemed to see the shadow of the suicide.

He retained also from that period another picture, rich in its symbolism—that of the guide who had pulled a ropeful of people to safety. It was in the summer of '42. He had asked for leave and secretly made his way to Chamonix with twelve hunted men. They were Jews: Austrians, Czechs, and Poles. There the priest turned smuggler, a "passer" of men at an altitude of nearly 10,000 feet.

"One has to live such an experience to understand it, to know what violent joy it can give. If one has known the breath-taking thrill of mountain climbing, of clinging to the sheer faces of ice-covered peaks, of traversing glaciers—the pure exaltation of prolonged effort, the final feeling of triumph over danger when one reaches the summit—one could then imagine the additional feeling of being responsible for the lives of twelve fellow men in such circumstances. There would come that instant when, after eight hours of marching, three of which were across glaciers, the guide could turn to his anguished companions who had placed their destiny in his hands and say: 'It's done! We are in Switzerland. You are safe.' The embraces, the expressions on their faces, the affection all felt for one another—these cannot be expressed."

At Emmaus, too, he had to pull others upward, until those who put their trust in him should say, "We are saved."

But such guides, such savers of men are rare.

The Father answered the seminarist, "We shall expect you. . . ."

13: *The Seminarist*
A Painful Chore

I came because I thought you would be pleased," said the
fat woman.

"I thank you," the Father said kindly, "but you shouldn't attend Mass just to give me pleasure, Madame Charles."

It was pouring rain on the morning of December 20. The
woman opened her umbrella over the priest's head as they left
the church.

"You are so alone," she said.

"But no . . . no, no, really."

They made their way to the porch. The seven-man team was
just leaving for the Clos Fleuri lot. They wore military raincoats
over their shoulders.

"I wanted to speak to you about my husband," said Madame
Charles.

"Come into the office."

The room was unheated. Mademoiselle had left for Vincennes, where she had found a secretarial job. At present the foundation had no other financial resources than her pay, the help of a
few friends of Emmaus, and the salary the priest received for
Mass.

"This is how it is, Father," said Madame Charles. "When we
came to the agreement about the land and the house at Clos
Fleuri, I had not told you all, but now you must know everything."

The warm, attentive look on the priest's face brought the blood rushing to her fat cheeks. She took a deep breath.

"It's difficult to tell you. But . . . but, we're not married, Charles and me. And we have two children, counting the two I had by my first husband, that makes four. I thought that if you found out we weren't married you might not want us to stay any longer."

The Father fell silent. He was thinking: "O God, how difficult it is at times to make them understand what we are trying to do and who we are."

"Please don't worry," he told her. "You needed help and it was our good fortune to be there to help you. As for the rest, I am not offering you a house in exchange that you be baptized or married in church."

She listened, nonplused.

"It was my husband, Charles, I mean, who said, 'Let's face it.' He doesn't like priests and things of religion."

"What we do is done not to be loved, but . . ." There he stopped for a moment. "What we do is done so there may be a few less people in misery and also so that the Lord should be a little better understood."

"Oh, how well you say that, Monsieur l'Abbé!" cried the fat woman with childish enthusiasm. "So don't be surprised if you haven't seen Charles yet, and when you meet him, please forgive him if he is shy and ill-mannered. He's not a bad man. He's a good father to the kids, to his own as well as mine. But I can't do a thing. He's always saying he'll never be caught talking to a priest."

"A pity," said the Father. "A priest is a man, too. Good people are few and far between, and if they never meet, how much lost joy . . ."

There were several timid raps at the door. The young seminarist poked his head inside, then withdrew it, closing the door.

"I'm leaving," said Madame Charles, "and thank you, Father."

"When do you move to Clos Fleuri?"

"This week, Father. We hope to be there for Christmas Eve. There are rumors of a strike in my husband's factory so maybe he'll have time to help with the moving. Luck, in a way."

She dropped her eyes and sighed.

"But I also wanted to tell you—it will be impossible for us to pay the installment this month. It's just a delay. We're sure next month it will go better."

"*Oui, oui.*"

She hesitated. Her eyes lost their slightly false smile, their cunning look. They filled with tears, and she murmured:

"This is just for a Mass, Father. For our youngest. He's crippled, his left foot is paralyzed. He was born that way. Could it be because we're not married? Charles and me? Tell me."

"God does not take that kind of revenge."

She stammered, sobbing:

"But Charles says that's exactly what He does do. That God is cruel, that He has no use for poor people."

Watching from his window as she crossed the court in the beating rain, the Father thought that this Charles must have suffered greatly. . . .

"Haven't you at least your driving permit?"

"No, Father."

"What do they teach you at the seminary? Come now, don't get in a state. Maybe soon I won't need my own permit any longer."

Mud caked the shoes and spattered the hem of the visitor's cassock. He had left Coulommiers that morning in a driving December rain.

Denis was a tall, lean youth with an arched nose, a willful chin, and stooping shoulders, his blue eyes shrouded with lids that gave him a solemn expression. His coarse hands and thick accent were those of a peasant.

"Well, I am happy to see you. But . . ."

The Father heaved a sigh.

"But what is it, Father? I hoped that my offer to work for you . . ."

"You were quite right to come, but the fact is that things are becoming extremely difficult."

He glanced at his desk piled with monthly bills.

"Mademoiselle, our secretary, was obliged to take on an office job."

Then suddenly he smiled. His eyes filled with delight, confidence, and strength.

"Well, it will all work out yet. You never know, but at the

very worst moments, with perfect timing, providential aid comes from Heaven. But you are frozen. Come and have something warm!"

They went down the porch. Rain had been falling steadily since the night before. In the kitchen, Alexandre and Baptiste were cleaning pots and pans.

"Father," said the chief cook, "we're out of oil."

"We'll boil the potatoes, then."

"And the coal is getting low."

The priest murmured: "I know, I know."

In Djibouti's workshop was a pile of old boards that would carry them over for another week. The Father's own office was not heated now. While Denis was drinking his coffee the Father, watching from the refectory window, saw a shadow slowly edging into the court.

"The fourth since yesterday," he murmured.

He stood up and went to the door. The man, wearing no coat and practically barefooted in torn sandals, carried a duffel bag at his side. He stopped, hesitated.

"Come in, come in," said the Father. "Alexandre, have you a bit of coffee left?"

The man touched his cap without taking it off, murmured a greeting, and sat down near the stove.

"Your vest is soaking wet," said the Father. "Is your shirt dry?"

The man opened his vest and disclosed a bare tattooed chest. He was shirtless.

He bit into the bread and drank the coffee.

"Got a smoke?" he growled.

Alexandre offered his pack. The man inhaled the smoke with great, avid breaths.

The young seminarist watched him, fascinated. What distress! What need! At last the man made an attempt to smile.

"Hiring any help?"

"Yes," said the Father, with a warm smile. "Some. What's your name?"

The man frowned. "Raoul, Raoul Del . . ."

"I want only your first name."

The man fumbled in his coat pocket, took out a paper folded in four, got up to hand it to the Father, who read:

"Father, kindly take in Raoul D. We can do nothing for him. Thank you. With my sincere good wishes I am, Yours in Christ."

It was signed by a nun, head of a foundation caring for ex-convicts and well known to the Father. On several occasions she had thus "favored" Emmaus.

"It wasn't my fault," growled Raoul. "I did four years at . . ."

"I am not asking you what you have done," said the Father, "but what you can do, what you will do here."

"Before I was just a laborer."

The Father smiled.

"Then you can be a lot of help here. But tell me, this note is dated three days ago. Why didn't you come straight here?"

"Don't know. I slept outdoors."

"Come, and you, too, Denis, maybe we can find something for both of you to wear in the 'store'!"

This was what he called a little room which had been filled up with gifts of underwear, bed linen, and clothing. It was in the cellar and had been the original quarters of the first men who lived at Emmaus the year before: Bastien, Djibouti, Étienne, and the Kangaroo. The shivering man had taken off his sopping vest and through the hair on his skinny chest the priest saw tattooed a dotted line passing around his neck like a necklace. It joined in an angle on his chest. At the point, inside a tiny circle, was tattooed an image of the Virgin.

"What's it supposed to be, your tattoo?" asked the Father, intrigued.

The man shrugged.

"When I was young, I was always losing the little medal my mother had given me. This way there's no chance of losing it."

Without his cassock, now dressed in a coat that was too short, wearing pointed shoes, Denis looked more like an awkward, overgrown youth, slightly comic and pitiful, a peasant come to the city.

"As far as hats go," said Abbé Pierre, "all I have is a bowler. They've been sent to me by the dozen—they're not in fashion just now."

"Let's see, Father."

In a corner someone had found an almost new windbreaker. The Father handed it to Raoul.

"Let me have yours," growled Raoul. "It's older than this."

"Never mind, take this one."

At the left of the main building a six-man team was putting up a dormitory that could contain twenty double-decked beds. One had to look ahead, with winter around the corner, for the growth of the community. In all there were fifteen men in the community at the moment. The Father called Filot, the colonial soldier who was responsible for the small building lot. He placed the two newcomers, the seminarist and the ex-prisoner, under his charge.

"Denis, in an hour I'll come to take you over to Clos Fleuri. For the moment there's the mail, and, you see, still another visitor."

Near the porch a fat woman and a man with a suitcase were waiting.

In the car on the way to Clos Fleuri the Father said to Denis:

"As to most of the men with whom you will be working, I could not tell you from where they come or who they are, nor even their real names. They tell us just what they want to. The less we question them on arrival, the less they are tempted to lie. The man who has been sleeping outdoors, who is hungry and cold, unless he's really strong, he will answer anything, anything at all just to be accepted and given shelter. It's only after a long time that they reveal their worth and tell us freely who they are."

After a short silence Denis asked:

"Why didn't Raoul come directly here when he left the foundation?"

The priest shrugged.

"Liberty, freedom after prison . . . he wanted to enjoy freedom even on an empty stomach, even in the rain. But you, Denis, tell me. I am permitted to question you. What made you ask the Father Superior for permission to come work with us for six months before being ordained?"

"My brother had told me about you. He has been to Emmaus several times on retreats."

"Yes, I know."

"It's both easy and difficult to explain to you, Father. Just now you asked me whether I could drive a car. I can't. But I can read

Greek and Latin, and I can explain the Gospels. The absence of true contact with life I've felt strongly. After eight years of study, away from everyone, I need to give that which no one ever asked for—I need to dive into real life like a grain of wheat in the earth."

"Yes," said the Father, "several young ones have said just that to me. But you must have more than just a passing enthusiasm. It will be very hard for you to take this, as you will soon see. Forget your Latin when you're with them and be concerned first with nothing but their suffering. Give them an example through your own work."

Denis looked at his hands, those large country boy's hands, reddish, but with a skin that was too smooth.

"And keep yourself good-tempered. You see, here, each one shows what he really is. Life is too hard for them to keep up pretenses for long. Here all must be sincere. And there will be no difference between your work and life and that of the others. You'll work with them, eat with them, sleep with them."

"Yes," said Denis, "and save myself with them, too."

"Do without everything as they do, too." Then dropping his voice the Father said, quietly:

"I don't know how much longer we can last. Don't tell the others that, though."

The rain had stopped when the car came to a halt by the embankment before lot Number 3. Five wooden houses stood in a neat row on the land. Marchand was now living in the gypsy wagon. Charles U., the communist, and Martinct were to move into houses Number 4 and 5 respectively within the next few days. On other lots building material was piled helter-skelter near the tents and wagons where the children were watching the rain. Two of the Emmaus men and Djibouti, protected by raincoats, were helping Michel, whose wife had been taken to St. Anne, to line up the bricks for the base of his house.

The Father made his way to the Vatier home. Marcel had surrounded his plot with an iron fence which also traced the outline of his small bit of garden. In the path which led to the porch he had laid pieces of ground brick.

"Come in."

Djibouti's dog came to sniff at the visitors and, recognizing the priest, started wagging his tail. In the tidy little room Madame Vatier was nursing her tiny Jeanne.

"Oh. Good morning, Father."

The stove threw out a welcome warmth. The light flowered wallpaper, the little pictures on the walls, the curtains in the windows, and the lace on the baby's crib gave the tiny home a clean, gay, friendly look. Finaud quickly found a warm spot by the stove.

"Please, won't you stay a moment?"

The mother buttoned her blouse.

"We're just passing by," said the Father.

"Just give me time to heat you some coffee."

Noëlle, standing on a chair, nose glued to the window, was looking outside.

"Aren't you coming to say hello?" asked the Father.

"Uncle Bouti," said the child, putting a finger on the window-pane in the direction where she could see the Emmaus team at work.

"She always wants to go with Djibouti. He's her great friend. When the weather's good she won't leave him."

"What do you want for Christmas?" asked the Father. "A rocking horse? A crib for your dolly?"

The child repeated, "Uncle Bouti."

The priest sat down near the stove. He was shaking with cold. "How does it go?"

"Everything's just fine, Father," said the young woman with a broad smile. "We have the rent money for you."

"That's not what I came for," said the Father. "But don't think I'm not pleased. That will let us help out more families."

"I know."

She looked at him with gratitude and affection.

"It's two months now that we've been settled here."

"You'll have to wait for the water. Have patience."

"Of course," said the young woman. "But we have the electricity in. If we start being difficult . . ."

"We'll start work again in the spring, if all goes well."

They drank the hot coffee.

"I always have some ready about this time for the men." Then, after a short silence: "By the way, Madame Marchand would like to speak to you. It's about one of your men, but she'll tell you herself."

Getting up to go, the Father took the little Jeanne in his arms.

"Good-by, Citizen Number 1 of Clos Fleuri."

The mother said softly: "Marcel and I have agreed about it, Father."

"About what?"

"The two girls haven't been baptized yet, and . . ."

"We'll talk about it later. Fine. Don't feel you're obliged to do so out of gratitude. You must realize the importance of your decision."

On leaving, he and Denis made their way to the gypsy wagon.

"Wait for me," said the Father to Denis. "Go and meet your future companions."

Not knowing how to introduce himself or how to start in with them, Denis slowly approached the lot and stood within a stone's throw from the workers, watching them.

"One more won't hurt," growled Djibouti. "Pass the bricks along."

Denis entered the line.

Twenty minutes later the Father came out of Madame Marchand's gypsy wagon and approached the group. His face was pale and stern.

"Where is Louis?"

"He left at nine o'clock," said Djibouti.

"Is he at the café?"

Djibouti shrugged in answer.

"I have to leave you, Denis," said the Father under his breath. "There's an urgent and disagreeable job to be done."

At the crossroads café, "the deserters" were playing a game of *bélote*. Embarrassed at the sight of Abbé Pierre, they behaved like children caught red-handed. "It's raining so hard, Father. We just can't work."

"Come with me, Louis."

Frowning, the husky youth took his cap, winked at his friends, and got into the car. They rolled along in silence.

At the crossroads after the Marne River the Father took a sharp right.

"Aren't we going back to Emmaus?" asked Louis.

"No, we're going to Paris."

"O.K."

The Father did not say a word until they approached the Vincennes gate.

"I'll drop you at Les Halles."

"Fine. Want me to run an errand for you?"

"No. I can't keep you at Emmaus any longer."

The youth gave a start.

"Why, what have I done? We can't work all day long in this lousy weather. It's because I . . ."

"It is not for sitting in the café that I am asking you to leave. You know perfectly well."

The youth sank into his seat. Then, after some minutes' silence:

"What will I do now?"

"What did you do before?"

"I worked for a plumbing and heating outfit, but there wasn't any business."

"You can look for work. I will leave you some money."

As they were going down the Faubourg St. Antoine, Louis said: "No use wasting your gas. Let me out here."

The car stopped.

"Listen, Louis," said the Father softly, "you must understand that if we have succeeded in sheltering these families it is not to torment them afterward. Madame Marchand must feel really safe and secure. You are twenty-five and I quite understand that a young woman alone . . . But you must get that out of your head, courageously. You owe us this sacrifice in exchange for what we have done for you."

"You say 'we,' " murmured the youth after a silence. "But it's you alone, Father."

"The community took you in. I acted only in the name of Emmaus. Each one of us must integrate himself, share responsibility, and give what he can. You must promise me you will never return to Clos Fleuri."

"What will become of me?" repeated the boy.

"Go now. If you cannot find work we will accept you at Emmaus fifteen days from now. You'll have time to think it over. As for your belongings, where do you want me to leave them for you?"

"Keep them."

He took the bills the Father handed him and murmured: "And . . . I understand, Father. You are right. Forgive me."

"You know very well you are forgiven. So long, Louis."

The car started off.

14: The Dark Days
Begging on the Street

THE WEEK before Christmas zero weather set in with bitter cold and frost. Of the Clos Fleuri workers, only two men went to the lot to finish papering the walls of the fifth house. This was Martinet's house and they were trying to get it finished so he could hold a housewarming for Christmas. Charles had already moved into his cottage, but the Father had not yet met his new tenant. They could not go on cementing the basement of Marcel's house with the thermometer at five below, so Djibouti took some time off. It was Christmas Eve. He shut himself up in his workshop, for he'd had an idea—something he wanted to get done by himself. He lighted the stove. Finaud was lying in his box nearby. Then he took the finest wood he had and traced the design of a little crib on wheels for Noëlle's doll.

For the last two days no one had seen the priest's ancient car. He had sold it.

"It can't last much longer now," thought Djibouti. "I'll finish making this toy, then I'll go ask the Father if he still really needs me."

And if the Father didn't need him, he'd have to hit the road again. This was what everyone called liberty—the dreadful servitude of liberty. At least his sorrow would be his own. He would not load the Father's shoulders with his troubles. He refused to be a liability. He could always get around Paris; he knew the ropes. Worst of all, though, would be getting back to the status

of the useless hermit, the shoe-dragging, going-nowhere, unwanted man, a man already erased from the books of destiny.
After Emmaus you couldn't quite go back and live as you did
before.

About three in the afternoon Filot entered the workshop and
sat down on a wooden box near the door. The two men were
about the same age. This was not all they had in common. Both
had lived out in the colonies and the war had crippled their
luck. Their characters and intelligence were superior to the situation into which they had fallen through circumstances. For ten
years Filot had directed an office in Madagascar. Placid, disillusioned, with a somewhat detached manner, he knew just how to
handle his men at Emmaus. It was not so easy now, though, with
the new additions; several older men had come to seek shelter
rather than work.

Just try and tell them that Emmaus isn't a poorhouse! The
Father wouldn't think of leaving them outdoors in this weather,
but their efforts are really not much and the wine bottle is always within reach.

"The dormitory is finished," grumbled Filot in his slow, husky
voice. "It's about time, too, let me tell you, because things don't
click any more, not one bit. I used to be able to make Arabs
work with blacks, but with these derelicts that come our way I
can't do anything. Can't get a lick out of them. I'd rather send
them over to the refectory to warm up and do the job myself. I
don't want to annoy the Father with these stories, but on the
days he's gone, like today, the young ones go off somewhere, too.
Go and look for them? Well, I just finished fixing the tin on the
roof, it's done, and they can all go to hell."

"The Father was out yesterday, too," said Djibouti.

"Yes, I wonder where?"

"Where d'you reckon he is? He's out looking everywhere for
money, so we can hold out another day. He sold the car day before yesterday, there's no more heat, and you know yourself what
there is to eat."

Without knocking, a man pushed open the door of the workshop. He was old, he had bright eyes and a beard, and a knap-
sack bag hung by his side. On his dirty stockingless feet he wore
shoes without laces.

"*Salut*," he said slowly. "I'm looking for the padre."

"The Father isn't here," said Filot with no enthusiam, thinking: "He has a mug like Rasputin's."

"Oh," said the man, disappointed.

He looked at the stove and started to cough.

"Come closer," said Djibouti. "Have you eaten?"

"No, and would it taste good!"

"I'll take a look in the kitchen."

Djibouti returned with a cup of coffee and a hunk of bread. The man had placed his bag beside him. He was stroking the dog and had just told Filot he was a ragpicker. An ex-boxer called "the Kangaroo" had told him about Emmaus in a café near the Rue Mouffetard. His name was Philippe. His back ached and he coughed. He was exhausted, and the trash cans just weren't full enough any more to keep him going. *La biffe* (ragpicking) is a hard business. To make a living you had to go at it thoroughly. When all was said and done, he just needed a little rest. Too bad to have to stop now, though, because Christmas and New Year's would really fill the garbage cans.

Filot said: "We work here; this isn't a poorhouse."

"I'm ready to work, too," said the old man, vexed. "All I ask is that nobody bullies me and that I get a bowl of soup a day."

He started to cough again.

The door opened. The priest. He looked thinner than ever, and his eyes were darkly circled. He limped heavily. Philippe stood up slowly.

"A new comrade," said the Father in a tired voice. "Have you found him a place to sleep?"

"The dormitory is finished," said Filot.

"Good. Have you any blankets left over?"

"I'll bring one down for him. There's also my sleeping bag which I'm not using just now."

The Father noticed the little cradle standing on Djibouti's carpenter's bench. It was almost finished.

"That's for little Noëlle," said Djibouti, visibly embarrassed.

"Excellent idea," said the Father.

Then after a short silence he said: "A good and excellent idea. We will give toys to all the children at Clos Fleuri."

His eyes brightened, his voice seemed to recover its force.

"And for every family a little pine tree."

"We can go to the forest of Armainvilliers. This will do the men good. It's bad for them to be idle."

In these last stormy days he had seen the spirit of Emmaus disintegrating from sheer inaction. Silently he had watched some of the men taking to drink, falling into inertia of body and spirit. Shivering, smoking, and grouped round the refectory stove, they would sit and talk like old habitués of poorhouses waiting for mealtime. When the newcomers came begging for work, the priest suffered at being able to give them only small chores. He understood how frustrated they felt at not doing enough to pay for their meals. Some of them had gone back, disappointed. They preferred to try their luck in Paris rather than exploit those poorer than they.

"Yes," said he, "we will organize 'Operation Christmas Tree.' "

"But they should be trimmed, these trees, decorated with sweets, oranges, bonbons, trinkets."

"Yes," said the Father pensively, "only . . ."

The three men saw what he meant.

"As for me," said Philippe, "I never eat dessert."

"We could go without a meal," said Djibouti.

It was then that young Antoine, who acted as orderly to the priest, came in to say that Abbé Pierre was wanted on the telephone.

This telephone call proved a decisive factor. In truth, the priest had for some time had this on his mind. His thoughts turned to it every time he felt an urgent, tragic case take him by the throat—the kind of case impossible for him to assist. For once there was really nothing he could do, neither shelter the family nor assist them financially. For the first time he felt completely helpless. A great anger had accumulated within him during these dreadful weeks against the scandalous differences in fortune, against the blindness of the rich, against the inertia he found in the city bureaus, and the limited means of the official organizations.

"Yes," he said to himself as he left Emmaus for Paris in answer to a call from Mrs. S. "Providence sometimes reveals itself

fifteen minutes too late in order to allow us to show our faith.
It always arrives, but . . . O God, in those fifteen minutes a
man may lose faith, kill himself and his family."

On the bus and in the subway he still seemed to hear the
desperate, anguished voice on the telephone:

"Hello, Father. I couldn't get you sooner. Please, please come
quickly. Last night I caught him at it again. He got up and had
turned on the gas to kill both us and the children. Come and
talk to him. *Only you can calm him.*"

The same sentence he had heard time and time again: "Only
you can save us." This confidence they had in him gave him
fresh confidence in God. He would not allow this suicide and
these murders to be committed. He entered the small hotel, went
on into a room paid by the month. There were three children.

"I haven't slept in a week," said the woman, sobbing. "I pretend to, but I'm too scared. This is the second time he's tried it.
I'm afraid to move. He's just gone out. He may jump into the
river."

The priest tried to comfort her, but he, too, was afraid. The
man, now completely a neurotic, could not reconcile himself to
the idea that they would soon be out on the street. In three days
they would have to leave the hotel. Their room cost 10,000
francs and his salary was only 22,000 francs. They had no money
left for food. The priest took out his last 500 francs. He gave it
all. He smiled at the three children, spoke to the woman, and
she seemed somewhat comforted. When the husband returned,
the priest promised to get him out of the jam. He didn't know
how yet, but if no other solution presented itself, he would take
them in at Emmaus. The husband promised to be reasonable,
but the look in his eyes remained distant, reserved, secret, the
look of a sick man.

"I will be back tomorrow," said the priest. "It will all work
out."

It will all work out. Oh, how he detested these vague promises,
empty, lying words when there seemed to be no hope.

The priest was suffering too much, he was too immersed in
the despair of others to overcome his own. He walked, his head
bent, through the crowd. He glanced automatically at a luxurious
shopwindow, a movie house, a packed café, at the line of shining

cars, the indifferent passers-by unaware of the scandalous misery all around them. If all men, thought the priest, so sure of themselves, so smug in their well-cut clothes and comfortable security —if each of them knew, if someone could explain to them that quite close by, even in the very buildings they live in, whole families could be saved by the same money that flowed so freely to movie box offices, stores, night clubs . . .

And words, sentences of imploration, curses formed in his brain. He quickened his step as he passed these strangers and almost murmured as if he were addressing this one or that one whom he brushed as he moved.

"You, who are passing, DO YOU KNOW . . .

"That in this twentieth century, in a country of science, of progress and supposed Christianity . . .

"Do you know this? The man next to you may be homeless or spending all his salary on one hotel room.

"Do you know that two steps from your door a baby will die tonight because his father has no money?

"For these poor thousands what good is life any more?

"Yet at the same time perhaps there are for you dividends, fun, stupid evenings, costing 10,000 francs per person.

"In all this folly and despair, WHO ARE YOU?

"What have you done to help?

"Yes, this is what I must say to them. I must make them understand. They will not remain indifferent if they know."

He crossed the Vincennes woods and the words seemed to cry out in the night, as if a multitude were singing them in chorus above the city. He knew of a small print shop. The owner would work quickly for him. Yes, it had to be quickly, for human lives were at stake.

It was late when he reached Emmaus. All was dark. In his own room, unable to sleep, he wrote down the first draft on paper. Oh, how different this was from the tract printed two years ago, decorated with pleasing photos (Entrance—Clos Fleuri— The Pond—The Park. Sun—Space. . . .) which made Emmaus a very tempting place for "a week-end at *Emmaus, center of social action and international relations, for days of study and prayer. . . .*"

Now Emmaus had become a home for the unhappy, and this

paper cried out their anguish, the despair of lonely people, of hunted families, a breathless, terrible anguish. It was a *De Profundis*, a cry so real that it should burst the hardest armor of egotism, should penetrate straight to the heart, a cry for help so profound that it should touch even the souls of the rich.

The priest reread his message. Having gotten it down on paper all ready to print, he felt less oppressed, almost delivered, but suddenly he murmured:

"Have I the right? Who am I to threaten the world with the wrath of God, like a prophet? To write 'Who are you, what have you done to help?' Am I worthy of accusing others of egotism? What have I done myself?"

When he was nineteen years old he had made a vow before St. Francis to accept a life of poverty. But for a priest or a monk to live in poverty, particularly in a monastery, appeared less difficult to him than the daily sacrifices which he must now make. From now on all peace would be unattainable because he had signed on paper this promise to the poor—a promise to consecrate his life to their salvation, alone, without help, without encouragement from anyone, like a partisan compelled by compassion.

From now on the spiritual resources which he might have devoted to political or diplomatic tasks would have no other object than an earthly struggle for a piece of bread, clothing, and a roof. Contemplative life, as well as public life, would be forbidden him. From now on, always on the alert, pushing before him an exhausted body, he would be a man of mercy. Would he hold out? The risk must be taken, for behind him all miserable people, including the ones at Emmaus, would be crying out for help with his voice.

Next day, hesitating over the choice of certain words, he showed the rough copy to an old friend, a wealthy bourgeois who had come to visit him at Emmaus.

The latter handed back the paper in stupefied horror.

"You're crazy! You can't say things like that."

"Is it a lie?"

"No. All you say is true, but this kind of thing should not be shouted from the rooftops as brutally as you are doing."

"Why not?"

"Because of the scandal. It's pure anarchy."

"Not at all. I am not asking people to oppose but merely to appeal to public authority."

"*All of you who can* . . .

"*So that all this suffering shall cease, struggle with all your might with the rich, with the state, with international authority, in one of the world organizations dedicated to this fight.*

"*Struggle so that the desperate may have the right to live.*"

"You're right, but you are *too* right. Life becomes impossible when you know all this."

He pulled out some franc notes from his billfold.

"Ask me for financial help, but don't ask me to suffer with them."

"My own object is not to suffer with them passively, but to achieve something for them, with them. All I ask is help, and, if possible, from the heart. To those who have everything I appeal for help for those who have nothing."

After a moment's silence his friend murmured:

"But between you and me, I don't quite understand why you are doing all this. Nothing obliges you to. Your health is not too good. Mind you, I am telling you all this in a spirit of friendship."

The Father was not indignant. He merely shrugged his shoulders.

"Of course. I know. But this has little to do with me."

If he had but asked, he naturally could have found a quiet post in a rest home or a chaplain's institution. But he was here and he was no longer his own master. He belonged to the poor, for he was their conscience, the conscience of their distress. He was the missile charged with the explosive of their suffering and guided by their necessity to revolt.

The tract was printed and delivered to the priest two days before Christmas. With the package under his arm he left for Paris during the afternoon, not telling his Companions of his plans. There was nothing to eat in the house and he did not want to build up their hopes.

No one will ever know what agony this begging on the streets was to him on that first day.

He started with the houses close to the Palais Bourbon at the end of the Boulevard Saint-Germain, hoping that his present job as a beggar compared to that of his former job as deputy would have a psychological effect, a brutal reaction on his former colleagues should he run into any.

He entered pastry shops, cafés, and grocery stores. His opening words, "I am not really a customer," froze the smile on the faces of salesgirls and owners.

In a few sentences he told of Emmaus where the unfortunate were in dire need of help that could not be refused them. Out of twenty merchants, five refused, telling him they were submerged by high prices, taxes, and financial burdens.

"If we had to help everyone that comes around here . . ."

And these were the same prices, taxes, and financial burdens that Abbé Pierre himself had voted. He was tempted to smile in his beard as he left the handbill which mentioned his rank of ex-deputy.

The package under his arm, he went up the Champs-Elysées. It was the *apéritif* hour. He planted himself, in his shabby windbreaker and mountaineer's beret, his cane and all his decorations, at the entrance of the most elegant cafés of the city. The evening was icy.

A few months before this he had been received by the Pope; innumerable times he had talked to the greatest men in international political circles; he was a close friend of cabinet ministers, his own ex-colleagues. And now, here he was a plain beggar, soliciting help from an indifferent public. "Living is more something you consent to than something you choose." Not only did he think this, but in his situation as beggar he saw and even admired the divine humor that lays out the curious pattern of life and makes each person play such a different role. Not only did he believe this, but he thanked God for having placed him there, for having picked him to cry out against undeserved suffering in the midst of implacable civilization and pagan feasting. To just this the vow of poverty pronounced in his youth had led, and now this vow was being renewed through the signing of this tract.

In their splendid furs, the most beautiful women in the world were stepping out of streamlined cars that glistened with chrome. They were followed by impeccably tailored men, calm, nonchalant, smiling: the princes of the earth. They crossed the pavement to where friends awaited them under the lights. They started to enter the cafés that rang with laughter, music, and chatter. Suddenly they were confronted by this black figure, this small, stooping man with a thin bearded face, wearing a torn windbreaker. He was offering them a piece of paper. One young woman stopped short for an instant, an instinctive gesture of re- fusal. She had at first taken him for a tramp distributing pub- licity forms. About to walk on, she suddenly noticed his cassock, his decorations, his look and his smile, neither obsequious nor ironical but kindly and calm. She did not understand, she was on her guard, and yet she felt filled with curiosity and a little fear before these eyes. He was not begging to music like the Salvation Army. This was something different. To this young woman the sincere priest evoked memories of a real, true world, and a distant face, forgotten, regretted, hated maybe: the Face of the Master, whom he seemed to resemble.

"Take one," she said to her escort.

Then man took the paper, gave it a glance. While reading it he continued to walk toward the café. Just as he was about to push the revolving door, he stopped, retraced his steps, took out his wallet, and handed the Father a bill. He then gave back the paper which was burning his fingers.

The paper burned many fingers on the Champs-Elysées that evening.

And then Abbé Pierre himself went into the de-luxe cafés. Possibly his passage spoiled the evening for many because of his allusions to "dividends, fun, and stupid evenings at 10,000 francs per head."

These heads did not care for the intrusion by this ambassador of the lower level into their world, the well-preserved world of the rich. But they did not dare ask the waiter to call a policeman for the Father was decorated: Legion of Honor, Croix de Guerre, Medal of the Resistance. In the extreme poverty of his station, his seven decorations constituted his sole protection against the hostility of the order he dared to trouble.

And then, with fatigue creeping upon him, little by little he felt overtaking him the slow tide of despair and the crushing

nausea of "what is the use?" It overwhelmed him suddenly as he
went back to the Boulevard Saint-Germain about midnight. He
had collected a little money, 2,000 francs, which would feed the
twenty unfortunates at Emmaus for one or two days. But after
that? What of the future? Well, if he had to he'd go down on
the streets and beg again.

But what really filled him with anguish and a kind of meta-
physical horror was the futility of it all. Even if twenty or so
derelicts were helped temporarily, what could he do for the multitudes of others? These, known and unknown to him, were
suffering by the thousands this very night and would continue
to suffer tomorrow and for a long time after. In the struggle for
themselves and for their children, under atrocious conditions, in
privation, blasphemy, and despair, there was no reprieve. He
could give them no direct help, these he mentioned in his tract.
The gesture of stretching out his hand to offer paper and receive
a little money, this gesture that cost him so much pain, how in-
finitesimal was the result. An isolated action, a voice in the
wilderness, all in vain, sterile. Still, the need remained so great.
So many steps, so many times "please" and so many times "thank
you"—all for a few hundred francs. This, when he would have
moved mountains to fight injustice. And the paper which they
took out of politeness, which they just scanned and then threw
away—could he hope that it would touch anyone's conscience?
And if this did happen, what great balance would the individual
revolt bring about? Everything would continue as before: selfishness, suffering, pleasure, despair. Here, money wasted. There,
money lacking. Indifference, laughter, grief, and death—and the
world would go on, blind to the truth. And whose fault would it
be? No one person could be blamed except, perhaps, several
powerful men who deliberately, with full conscience, fostered
their own fortunes even though they knew this might one day
lead to universal ruin.

A small street just off the lighted boulevard—a small street
with no shops and closed shutters was where Abbé Pierre went
in the darkness to hide his emotion. Leaning against the wall,
exhausted and on the verge of collapse, he bowed his head and
closed his eyes in absolute desolation. He felt the overwhelming
sorrow that was crushing his shoulders. O God, O God! He gave

ABBÉ PIERRE

Emmaus,
where
Abbé Pierre
first
received
the homeles[s]

Funeral of
a child
who froze
to death in
the shell
of an
abandoned
bus

After Abbé Pierre's broadcast, those without shelter allowed to sleep in the subway stations

A group of Abbé Pierre's men, the Ragpickers

Sorting out a dump heap

Bottles from the dumps to be resold

A plea for the homeless

A Paris concierge cleans out the attic

Plans for the Emergency City

He has never
had a home . . .
watching as
the new house
rises

A child
in better
circumstances
bringing his
bear to
Abbé Pierre's
collectors

One of the
homes built
by Abbé Pie
men

Shrine of
Our Lady o
the Homele

Picture Credits:
Photo J. Beauvi
Photo Emmaus,
Photos Match,
Photo J. L. Cra
and Courtesy of
Edna Bennett

way, lost heart, he could go on no longer. Huddled against the blind wall, he wept, and the tears eased him a little. Then he pulled himself together.

"No, this had to be done. This had to be. Even with an insignificant result, this sign had to be given."

He left the shadow, gathered up his courage for another try. He spotted a little café, still open—the movies were already out. The bistro was almost empty, just one customer and the proprietor left. The customer stood silent, staring into space. Leaning on the counter, he was lost in a dark reverie.

The priest handed him his paper. The surprised man took it, read it, and while the fat proprietor was complaining to the questing priest about rates and taxes (so heavy that small shopkeepers were practically starving), the lone man looked at the priest. Probably from timidity he made no gesture.

On leaving the café Abbé Pierre turned around. The man's eyes were still fixed on him, and the priest was never able to forget that look, so intense, so desperate. The man seemed to beg for conversation, yet he did not dare make the first move.

Next day in his mail the Father found a tract on which had been written these lines:

"Yesterday I met a priest in the Boulevard Saint-Germain. This meeting made me turn back to the God of my youth. Thank you."

There was no signature. Could it have been the stranger in the café? A modest gift of 100 francs was attached. It seemed to the priest somehow more precious than any of the other larger bills given with indifference.

The priest kept the scrap of paper received from the stranger. It was to him an anonymous assurance that his effort had not been in vain, a symbol that perhaps all the other unknown people would feel the same. It seemed to be the answer to the "what is the good of it all?" that was torturing him in the deserted streets. And in the course of the next few days other answers came in, one after another, and they made up for his grief.

The Father attached the paper to the head of his bed. He keeps it there still like a letter of credit on Providence.

15: *Christmas at Clos Fleuri*
The Craft of Ragpicking

WITH the few francs gleaned from the priest's pre-Christmas begging, the community held out for a few more days. They were even able to buy modest presents for the Clos Fleuri children and small decorations for the tiny trees brought back with them from an expedition to the woods. On Christmas Eve, Abbé Pierre, accompanied by his team, made the rounds of the gypsy wagons, the tiny houses, and the tents.

That very morning the Martinet family had moved into the fifth bungalow and the Father had yet to meet the tenant of the fourth, this man Charles who had such a hatred for priests.

It was freezing. A fine snow had fallen during the day. They rapped at the doors just as the children were going to bed, and because there was not room for them all to get inside the houses, the Father entered with just those who were carrying the tree. Outside, the others could hear the joyful squeals of the children and through the windows they could see the happy faces of the families they had helped shelter.

First of all, a round was made of the families with children: the Vatiers, the Spanish woman, Madame Marchand. Soon the group from Emmaus was scattered all over the development visiting various homes.

The families met for the first time the newcomers to Emmaus, offered them a drink while these lonely souls took the children on their knees, played with them, and with their awkward voices joined them in songs. So from one end of Clos Fleuri to the other, in this lost corner of God's earth, they visited the little houses, the gypsy wagons, and the tents. Through the exchange of good will and humble pleasure, the priest's workers introduced the atmosphere of a family holiday. And to a man they were conscious of the spirit of Emmaus which had given them security and conferred upon them this new dignity.

The Father had decided to visit Charles alone. Should the man insult him, at least there would be no witnesses. Carrying the festooned tree in his arms, he knocked at the door. It opened and the man on the threshold stared at the visitor.

"Merry Christmas," said the Father.

Behind the immobile man the priest could see his wife clearing the table, the four children looking wide-eyed at the mysterious guest carrying the glistening tree. Charles said in a low voice:

"Is it you, Father?"

He stepped aside.

"You are the first priest I've ever let cross my threshold. But you're different. Come in, Father; you are at home here."

And when the Father took leave of them twenty minutes later, Charles accompanied him across the snow-covered garden as far as the fence, and shaking his hand he said:

"I don't believe in the God of others. For me, Father, the Bon Dieu—God, it's what you are doing."

Several of the men, like Djibouti, who stayed to visit the Vatiers, lingered on at Clos Fleuri. The others, weary, went back to Emmaus.

The Father in his turn made his way to sing Mass at the Emmaus chapel. He stopped by the Martinets', where their light was still burning. The children were in bed, the mother was sewing curtains for the windows. Martinet, who was sitting by the table where the small tree stood sparkling, got up as the priest entered. His face wore an expression that was strange and haggard at the same time. The priest noticed it.

"Why, what's wrong?"

The man remained silent at first, then his chin started to tremble, his eyes filled with tears, and he stammered:

"I was thinking, Father. This is the first time in my life that I've had a home I can call my own."

He was a native of the north of France, one of nine children.

"It's the first time in two years of marriage that my wife and I have been alone in a room together, that we have been in our own home. Before there were ten of us in one room, counting the brothers and parents. I couldn't ever be alone with my wife except in summer when we would leave and go spend the night in the woods."

But the word of salvation, the material salvation of Emmaus, came from one of the last arrivals—from Philippe the ragpicker. He pronounced the words of grace several days later.

On December 29, with Christmas over, the dark days of privation came again. The Father went out to beg once more. He returned exhausted at about seven o'clock. By the stairs he met old Philippe who was sweeping up pools of wet snow.

"Can you come in a minute?" the Father queried.

They entered the cold office. Abbé Pierre emptied his pockets onto the table. Together they counted the heap of bills and coins —1,300 francs.

"Maybe that will do for tonight and tomorrow. Will you take it to Alexandre? Tell him to buy sardines, bread, and some wine that we can mix with water."

During the meager meal that he shared with them in the refectory the Father looked at each of his companions one by one. It was a long look filled with affection and pain.

Djibouti, the "Bear," the silent one, who was now the veteran since Bastien had been hospitalized; Filot, the colonial, once worth millions; Jacquot, the young workman, jobless, who like two other comrades had been forced to separate from his family because of the housing crisis; young Dédé, an orphan; and Pierrot who had run away from home because he was continually being beaten by a drunken father. Then there were the stateless ones, political refugees with no papers; two exiled Spaniards, and Kurt, an ex-professor from Central Europe who had escaped from a left-wing government. There was Raoul, the old lawbreaker, and Serge, who on his return from Buchenwald had gone back to his accountant's job and then dipped into the cashbox; the three French veterans of Indo-China; Gabi with the face of an artist (the priest knew little about him except that he had once been on the stage under a different name and had been fairly well known); and Lurson, the aristocrat, always well groomed, who could never get used to saying "thou" in the familiar French style to his comrades; Alexandre, the cook, was once a wool salesman. His wife's departure had upset him so much that he gave up his job. At Emmaus he seemed to have regained his equilibrium. And then there was Patoche (the nickname was all the priest knew), the drowning man they had pulled out of the river; and Donat, the American Negro, maybe AWOL; Denis, the seminarist who, in joining them in a surge of faith, had possibly not realized the going would be so hard; Philippe, the ragpicker, and the three or four men who preferred a precarious freedom to the workhouse.

The Father refused to call them "fallen ones," culprits, failures, or tramps. In them he saw specifically victims of the war, of social injustice, of sickness, of destroyed homes, of heredity, of their education. They were men who had been hit by misfortune, but always, in spite of everything, had remained worthy of confidence. Some were alcoholics, others were old delinquents, still others incapable of adjusting themselves to a regular job. Society refused them every chance of salvation, but the Father did not judge them this way. For him a man was never lost. He was ready to put his faith in the soul that lived beneath the rags. So humane he thought, so grateful (though they rarely said thank you), so devoted, so friendly, so fundamentally generous —so many things more than others who called themselves good Christians (and it was mostly because they had suffered and thus were more sensitive to the suffering of others).

"And now," thought the Father, looking at the helpless faces of his flock, "what can be done? Construction has been stopped. I cannot feed them any longer. Should I disband them tomorrow? Where can they go? On the street where they will be arrested for wandering? Or, better, place them in the idleness of a charity foundation? Send them to miserable solitude after having offered them a little warmth, security, friendship, and work? A home? Those who say: 'The priest, he's sincere, he eats with us, sleeps on the ground as we do, works with us.' Will I betray their trust? Tomorrow, if no help comes, should I say to them, 'We have nothing . . . we must part'?"

Next morning Philippe (called Rasputin) knocked on the office door.

"Father," he said in his hoarse voice, "maybe I ain't so much, but some things I see right clear-like."

"What do you mean?"

"Fact is, I caught on yesterday about how you raised the cash to feed us."

"Well, if you did, keep it to yourself. The main thing is . . ."

"No, Father, if you'll hear me, Father, seems to me we *must* talk about it. By taking me in, you saved me. Now I want to help you to save others, too."

"What do you mean, Philippe?"

"I was a *biffin*—a ragpicker."

A ragpicker. One of those poor devils one sees at dawn before the city street cleaners go to work. They fish in the trash cans with a long hook and stuff their repulsive harvest of bones, paper, and garbage into a dirty bag. How can one make a living from that, from that miserable task he calls a skilled craft? And he thinks he can help the Home?

Without putting much faith in the idea the Father let him go down to Paris in the freezing dawn to try his trade with an iron hook—a trade more precarious than that of a beggar.

That evening Philippe put on the priest's desk a 500-franc bill.

"This is for the Home, Father. This is what I made."

"With your scavenging?"

"Yes, Father, and I have a full bag still on hand."

"Well, then, it's serious, this garbage-can business."

"Let me explain, Father. Ragpicking isn't always a tramp's business like you might think. You can call it by a fancier name —'salvaging.' It's a way to get raw material for industry. But you gotta know the ropes to organize, if you know what I mean. You can't tinker at it; you gotta try to reach the higher brackets. You gotta be able to stock the material, do without the middleman, and sell it wholesale."

The priest suddenly felt that his famous "fifteen minutes of Providence" had passed with the last day of the year.

"But to whom do you resell this ash-can produce?"

"I know dealers and half wholesalers. If you want I can give you their names."

And Philippe initiated the priest into the technicalities of the ragpicking profession. It could be broken down into types: *la chine* and *la biffe*—house-to-house begging and trash-can digging.

"My specialty is the *biffe*: digging into the cans. Not because I prefer it to the house-to-house kind, but just because I'm not organized. A guy who works alone, who hasn't got any place to sort out his stuff and clean it and stock it, has to depend on the half wholesalers, and he never makes much. But he has to go through them because the factories don't buy rags, paper, and metal by the kilo [1] but by the ton. And this way prices can be doubled. In bulk, paper sells at four francs or more a kilo. A single worker like me hasn't got a chance; he can't discuss prices. And more often than not the poor devil fishin' in the garbage is a drunkard. He's glad to swap a full sack for a liter of wine, and the half wholesaler who gives him the wine gets rich quick.

"I know the chief of a bunch of ragpickers—poor bums, they got took for a ride—but this guy turned into a millionaire in three months. And those were prewar millions, too. Now, instead of fumblin' around, they're organizin' young, hefty workers, fast and on the ball. They're really somethin'—real go-getters. The whole family works. They stock the stuff, repair it, and sell it themselves, wholesale and retail. In winter, they're diggin' in the ash cans. In summer they're in Biarritz, drivin' Cadillacs. Believe me, it's the truth. They repair bicycles they pick up in pawnshops, and deal in secondhand cars. On top of that they raise chickens and pigs—they feed them cabbage roots, vegetable peelings, bits of dry crust, bones, and mildewed bread. Butchers let them have stale meat, the greengrocers give spoiled fruit and vegetables. I know an old ragpicker, not too fussy, of course, who lives entirely off of garbage. You can get something out of almost anything you find in an ash can—metal, tin cans, rags, paper, glass, rubber, bones, vegetables, bread. All you leave is ashes, rubbish, and odds and ends that are too far gone."

"And the *chine*?"

[1] Equal to 2.20 pounds.

"That's door-to-door salvage."

Over the years, attics, sheds, cellars, and corners of houses get piled up with unused objects—things that were useful and valuable but now just dying a slow death. Cracked mirrors, heirlooms, blackened doodads that once were wedding presents, armchairs with broken legs, moth-eaten curtains, collections of old magazines, books gnawed by mice, old clothes, pieces of dresses that are out of fashion, awful-looking junk of a former golden era, chipped picture frames, boxes, cases, all that which time, worms, and rats can get into and which is slowly turning to dust: that's it; that's the dealer's happy hunting ground.

Not so long ago in Paris one used to hear the junkman in the courts and narrow streets. His cry was melancholic, like a plaintive chant: "Rags and scrap iron for sale (*Habits, chiffons, feraille à vendre*)." If today he sings no more, he still goes by knocking at doors, going up and down stairs to the various floors. His potential customer may be moving, or in need of a little money; or maybe he has simply noticed something he had tucked away years ago and decides it is now only taking up room; and it may bring in something. . . . The old maid in need suddenly attaches, just as she is parting from it, an immense value to her chimney cloth or to a deep armchair brought from her childhood home. But an article's sentimental value does not always correspond to its market price. The ridiculous price offered by the dealer sometimes scares them. Then sometimes a customer asks the junkman to clear out a dusty cellar, a job the customer himself hasn't the courage to tackle. Sometimes the junkman accepts the discarded loot as pay. He sells it and often, too, he gets an extra tip for the cleaning job.

In his bag, in a baby carriage, in a pushcart, often in his own truck, the dealer takes away his assorted loot. He repairs what can be salvaged and sells it to Flea Market dealers, secondhand shops, or others. Or, having broken up the object, he separates the metal from the wood, the leather or plastic, sorts the rags and paper (and the better this sorting is done, the more interesting the sale price will be), and sells the raw material to wholesalers, or directly to factories at officially established prices.

In telling the story of the ragpicking and junk-dealing professions, Philippe had omitted certain details that Abbé Pierre and his men learned through practice and often through painful experience. In the beginning the Father was not too convinced that this profession would ever amount to anything, but he felt the experience was worth a try.

"Father, if you like, tomorrow some of us could give it a go. It's New Year's Day, and there's sure to be a harvest in the ash cans."

On the day following a holiday, the ragpickers reap thousands of anonymous gifts: bottles emptied during the night, canned foods with the contents only half emptied, things that have been thrown away as new gifts replace the old, clothes, jewels, lost keys (these are returned and often a good tip is received), broken vases. So much happens on a holiday that the ragpicker surveying disdained treasures often makes strange discoveries which lend to his grimy profession a spirit of adventure.

"I'll take Djibouti along, he's an old vagabond, and I'll take a younger one, too—Dédé, if he wants to go. We'll cover the suburbs. Paris is too far."

Next day the community was still sleeping when Philippe and his two ragpicking apprentices left Emmaus with their sacks and went out on their job. The following day there were four of them, pushing a child's perambulator.

On the fourth day the Father said:

"There's no longer a problem."

But there was a problem, in fact there were quantities of problems.

On the fifth day came the first obstacle.

16: *Fishing in the Trash Cans*
A Clash

D AY had not yet dawned as they started down the avenue. The snow, half melted the evening before, had frozen again in the night and it crunched under the boots of the five Companions. The middle of the road was black, but the sides were piled with soft white mounds, gleaming faintly in the light of the street lamps. Along the road small houses, all dark and closed tight against the cold, seemed to disappear into the mist. Between the banks of snow the sidewalk was a narrow icy path, but here and there in front of the doors spots of cinders and soot offered the men a temporary safe footing.

Pushing the perambulator through the hardened ruts of snow and ice, the Emmaus ragpickers silently crossed the sleeping suburb. Guided by Philippe, they headed for the café at the crossroads of the national highway.

"It opens at seven," said Philippe to the silent group. "We might get a drink there to warm us up before startin' the job."

They quickened their step. Soon they saw glowing through the mist a halo of blue light, the first neon sign on the main highway. They crossed over at the intersection and headed for it. Their collars turned up against the damp cold, the sacks across their shoulders, Philippe and young Dédé walked in front, followed by Djibouti and Denis, the seminarist. The latter had one hand on the handle of the perambulator—its wheels seemed to be keeping time with their step. Raoul, the man with the tattooed medal, lagged behind, browsing over some old dream.

On the snow-crusted road cars filed past toward Paris. Large cars carrying businessmen, owners, employers, two big trucks that were trying to get to the food market in time, little delivery trucks belonging to the vegetable growers and Brie cheese merchants.

A hundred yards ahead now was the glow of the café's neon sign.

Djibouti stopped for a moment. His leg had already started smarting. He lit a cigarette, handed one to Raoul. The latter had his eye on a bus going to Paris. His thin, sad, clown's face wore a strained smile, his slit eyes were laughing, really laughing, as he watched the bus disappear in the fog. Djibouti understood the smile on the ex-prisoner's face—to get to Paris, blend into the obscurity of the city, walk freely along the streets—there, and only there did liberty make any sense.

"You feel good about a jaunt to Paris, eh?" said Djibouti.

"You said it."

"Emmaus isn't so bad, though."

"That's not what I mean."

They started off again toward the café. Raoul was pushing the perambulator. Denis plodded silently along beside him on a slippery path.

"The city suffocates me," said Denis.

"Ah, you're just a stick-in-the-mud," said Raoul, "just a little priest who's a stick-in-the-mud."

Then he gave the silent youth a nudge in the ribs and grinned without malice.

"I'm only raggin'. We've gotta loosen you up somehow."

"I know that," said Denis. "And in a way you're quite right. I don't know the city and, just as you say, I should get broken in."

While he was drinking his jigger of rum, Philippe told them he knew the corner "dealer" who never got in before seven. The city garbage collectors came by about one hour later.

"The 'dealers'?" questioned Denis.

"The regular ragpickers. They carry a permit from the city

to go through the garbage before the city truck comes round. They carry a carpet, a bag or square of oilcloth so they can spread out their loot. Each man has his sector. See, I have my card for Paris from the Prefecture of Police, but my section is Ranelagh —Rue de la Pompe. That's a beautiful section—far richer than this. This card's no good out here, though." And he put the card back in his torn coat.

"Let's hurry now. No use clashin' with the regular guys and the garbage collectors. I can see the dustbins out there now, just waitin', you might say."

They emptied their glasses and divided up into two teams. Philippe and Dédé took the left-hand side of the street, Djibouti and Raoul the right.

"You, Denis, you're the fussy one. Fishin' in garbage is gonna turn your stomach. You push the pram and follow."

"I've turned manure on my father's farm," the seminarist said. "And all we must say to ourselves is that this isn't garbage but money for Emmaus."

"I always think of the lad who found a 13,000-franc pearl necklace."

"Did he return it?" asked Denis.

"Why, of course. You bet your life," said Rasputin with a little laugh. "But let's get on with it. Enough talk."

Each team took away three sacks full. By hand and by hook the men rapidly explored the contents of the ash cans. If it seemed worth while and the can was not too heavy they would turn it upside down into their sacks. Sometimes they would spread out the garbage and sort out the "good." More often they skimmed the surface without turning it over, extracting rags, papers, cans, bottles, setting aside vegetable peelings and household dirt. Once their bag was filled, they took it over to the perambulator.

In this way they covered most of the boulevard. Farther on, beyond the commercial downtown streets, came the residential section, and the contents of the cans seemed to change. There they found leftovers, butter from meals, even chicken. There were bits of cake, half-decayed fruit, a few broken and unwanted toys, bunches of dead flowers—carnations, roses, violets—remnants of New Year's parties.

"Nothin' excitin'," growled Philippe. "Let's take the apples, anyway."

And when Dédé made a face, he added:

"Until you've eaten what you find in a garbage can, you'll never be a real ragpicker."

Now the street lights went out. The daylight seemed pallid. The overcast sky announced an imminent snowfall. In front of a drugstore they found a little lacquered box, black and gold. It appeared intact and was empty. Just the lock had been broken. Three houses farther down they picked up an old typewriter, a 1910 model, with some keys missing. They carried it to their cart. On the other side of the road Djibouti and Raoul discovered a child's scooter with pedals, a lady's still-good handbag, a pair of pants, a little leather picture frame.

"It's beginning to work, I can see. I can feel that 13,000-franc necklace comin' up any minute now," Philippe said under his breath. By now the collector's fever had really seized Dédé. No sooner had the lid come off a can than he was plunging his hand into the doubtful mess of greasy rags and peelings. Suddenly the boy let out a yelp.

"Good God," said Philippe, "didn't I tell you to let me get in there first with my hook?"

Dédé withdrew his hand, showing a piece of broken bottle still stuck into his palm. The blood slowly started gushing.

"You'd better go and wash it quick. It might get infected."

It was just then that the "dealer" appeared at the end of the street. In the fervor of their quest the Emmaus ragpickers had lost all notion of time.

It was eight-thirty when Philippe caught sight of the small man wearing a goatee and spectacles and looking more like a bureaucrat than a ragpicker. Had it not been for his sack, his hook, his dirty coat and cap, Philippe might not have recognized him. The man stared silently first at Philippe and at Denis, and then his glance turned to the others.

"Might as well face it," said Philippe.

"*Bonjour*, Antoine."

The other replied furiously:

"What the hell are you doing out here, Philippe? Isn't your section the Rue de la Pompe?"

"Yes, it is. But let me explain . . ."

The man looked quickly around and then speaking in an undertone and without venom:

"You louse! You're in luck today. It's Monday and the wife's along. She'll be here any minute. And you know her."

"O.K., Antoine. I'm in the wrong, I know, but take it easy, I'll make it up to you one day with a bottle of wine."

He turned to the others and said:

"Come on, boys. Rightabout-face. Let's get goin'."

Dédé, his hand still bleeding, picked up the sack. They crossed the street to join Djibouti.

"Guess that's all for today," said Philippe.

Denis turned the go-cart around.

"Hey, you," a voice called after them. "You sneaks. Just let me catch you poaching around here again . . ."

The noise of a motor drowned out his voice. Around the corner came the city garbage truck. It did not resemble the modern Sita's used in Paris, those huge closed boxes into which garbage is drawn through a large jaw of iron teeth that appears to masticate the food. In most suburbs the garbage collectors still use a plain open-back truck.

The two garbage men, running at each side, grabbed the heavy ash cans with a quick gesture and threw them at the cleaner, standing in hip boots on the platform in the midst of all the litter. The latter, after quickly turning the cans upside down, tossed them back just as quickly onto the pavement. The empty pails clanged like so many cracked bells. The truck went on to the next door and while on its way the garbage cleaner made a first rapid survey with his hook, retrieving rags, metals, paper. He tossed these into various bags hanging on the side of the truck by the driver's seat. This operation would continue until they reached the garbage dump and even there the sorting would continue. The harvest would then be divided between all the men on the truck: the driver, the runners, and the garbage collector.

Turning around, Philippe saw Antoine's wife stop one of the men who were working on the truck, a tall, lean fellow wearing a red sweater. He saw her point to the group from Emmaus. The truck stopped. The runners went up, too, to hear the woman's complaint. Then all of them went up to speak to their driver who had stuck his head out of the cab window. The man in the red sweater beckoned to Philippe.

"Wait for me," the Emmaus leader said to his companions. "Let me settle this." Shaking his head, he grunted under his breath, "It sure would be a pain in the neck to have to leave them all this loot."

He walked up to the garbage truck, his hands in his pockets. Poking his head out of the window, the driver, looking like a judge in his box at a law court, said to him:

"Antoine's wife is griping because you . . ."

"Yes!" screamed the woman ragpicker. "He brought his whole team out here to poach. I'd just like to know what right he has . . ."

"Are you a ragpicker?"

"Yes, I have my card," answered Philippe.

He took the card out very slowly, so everyone would have time to calm down.

"Anyway, this ain't his ground," shouted the woman.

The driver looked at the card.

"Say, this is only good for inside Paris."

"Look," said Philippe. "If we're doing this job, believe me it's not for us."

"I don't give a damn who it's for," shrieked the woman. "They have at least eight sacks full. Look at them."

"It's for the Home at Emmaus," said Philippe, ending his sentence.

"The Home at Emmaus? Wait a minute," said the driver. "You mean for the priest who's building Clos Fleuri?"

"Sure. Do you know him?"

"I'll say I do. My brother bought a plot of land from him. He's built himself a house— Charles, maybe you know him?"

"Yeah, sure I know him."

"But that don't help us. And it don't give us back what they poached from our grounds," the woman started over again.

"That's enough," said the driver. "Look here, you can pay Antoine off; give him 200 francs. But you can tell the priest not to send you out here again. It's lucky you met me."

"O.K.," said Philippe. "I'll tell the Father."

And Abbé Pierre, to prevent a recurrence of this clash with the garbage collectors and "dealers" who enjoyed a city-bestowed monopoly on garbage salvage, decided to concentrate on *la chine,* secondhand dealing. He had a paper mimeographed and distributed to all the mailboxes in the neighborhood, advising everyone that the collectors from Emmaus would be around. At the end of the first morning Philippe returned with his team and told the priest:

"Father, there's so much stuff out there I couldn't bring it all back. We'd better all go down there."

So the priest called all the Companions together, and in a group they made the rounds. From that day in mid-January junk dealing became the basic industry at Emmaus. It permitted them not merely to exist independently but to help finance the building lots which were under construction.

17: *André, the Engineer*

T HE CONCIERGE of Number 7 reread the little mimeographed paper that he had found in the apartment-house
mailbox.

> To subsidize the needs of the Home of Emmaus (*sheltering*
> *the homeless, building homes, etc.*) *the Home is collecting scrap*
> *metal, old papers, rags, clothing, shoes, bottles.*
> The collectors will come by on January 14. Any contributions
> *will be gratefully received.*

"What do we do with this?" he asked his wife, handing her
the paper together with the mail for distribution to the tenants.

Ads, notices of sales, he found them by the dozen every month
in the mailbox. Generally they went straight into the waste-
basket. Memos announcing the visit of gas and electricity meter
readers were pinned to the bulletin board in the hall. But this
had him baffled. "You don't usually throw out something to do
with a religious foundation—it might bring bad luck anyway.
I'd better show it to the boss's wife."

Then the two of them got down to sorting the mail.

"Look. Here's a letter from Argentina for the engineer," he
said. "I'll ask him to save the stamp for me."

His wife took the package of mail, went up to the first floor,
and rang the proprietor's doorbell. Madame Gilbert answered
the door herself. She was pretty, about thirty-five, a good-

humored woman who came from the south. Her husband, general manager of a large export concern, was often away on business. He was on the road most of the week, visiting his company's branches in the large seaports.

"Do we put this up, Madame?"

The proprietor's wife read the paper.

"Emmaus," she said. "But I know all about that! My husband knows the Father quite well," she cried with enthusiasm. "The 'builder-priest.' So they're coming tomorrow? We must give them a good reception. But I will see to it myself."

She kept the paper. The concierge's wife thought that it would be hard to find a nicer lady to work for and went on distributing the stack of mail. On her way downstairs she met a young girl, the engineer's fiancée. She was from a good family, if one could judge by the fur coat she wore. Might even be a future tenant. The two women exchanged smiles.

André, the engineer, was just reading his letter from Argentina when the bell rang.

"I've brought you a new book," said his fiancée. "It's just been published. I haven't read it, but I liked the title. It will be a change from your *Political Economy.*"

André slipped his hands into the girl's warm fur sleeves, kissed her temple which smelled of perfume.

"Mind my hair-do," murmured Jeanne.

Then slowly leaving his embrace, she said, "I'm going to take you home to lunch. Mother and Father are out. Or shall we go to a restaurant? You're so quiet, André. What's wrong?"

The young man picked up the letter from Argentina.

"It doesn't seem to be working out the way we hoped, Jeanne."

"What doesn't?"

"Our trip to South America."

"Well, that's all right with me," she said. "And it doesn't change our plans of getting married by Easter. We'll simply stay in Paris, that's all."

"You're right; it doesn't change anything, except that I hoped . . ."

He offered her a Virginia cigarette and a glass of port.

"I don't know why, but the factory is getting on my nerves."

"Oh, please," said Jeanne lightly. "You're no longer a student."

The young man sighed. "Sure I'm not. I'm twenty-four, and the boss's son, but I can't breathe in the plant, physically or morally. The stink of soapsuds, of synthetic essences, work in the lab, or in the office. And then the organization of the work itself; I don't agree with Father . . ."

"Don't be absurd."

"The exploiting of personnel. I've checked the figures. The sales price of a cake of soap when it leaves the plant, the share that the worker . . ."

"You'll make it worse if you mix politics into this. All you should be interested in is your share, which is what we'll be living on soon."

She added, smiling: "Future director and future father of our children."

She went up to him and ran her fingers through his hair.

"Come on, let's get some air."

"Yes, it's getting serious," he said soberly. "Your perfume, do you know what it reminds me of?"

"It's called 'Gypsy Laughter.' I suppose that's what it makes you think of."

"No, it reminds me of a working-girl, and she doesn't think it's funny. You see we make the perfume and yesterday I looked at her bottling it. From morning till night she makes this motion."

His right hand imitated the gesture of taking an empty bottle, of holding it under a tap.

"With the left hand she presses a lever and then she passes the filled bottle to the next worker who screws on the cap."

"And so she goes, at top speed, hour after hour, day after day. I wonder what she thinks about all day."

"That she's earning her living."

"Enough to pay for meals, her bed, and not much else. Life should mean something different. One should have a little free time to enjoy it."

Jeanne shrugged her shoulders.

"You annoy me. Get your father to buy a machine and let's hear no more about it."

"And the woman will be unemployed when the machine does all the work."

"Stop it, André. That's life. There's nothing one can do about it. In the meantime your perfume worker is doing a far more savory task than a ragpicker."

"You bet she is. But that's the awful part about it all. There are so many who are so much more unfortunate."

"Must I think of all that when I go shopping? I'll end by lacking the courage to enter a shop at all."

"On the contrary, your role is to buy as much as possible."

"Because my parents are wealthy? Is it a sin to be wealthy?"

"Maybe," he said.

They looked at each other. There was silence, five seconds of acute silence, as sharp and painful as a blade separating two people, two destinies. . . .

"All because of your perfume, and because I love luxury, you hate me," said Jeanne in a low voice.

She always liked to bring things to a head, to clarify a situation and create the irremediable.

"Why, for heaven's sake?" But in his voice there was a troubled note. Her gloved hand made a little gesture—unexpected, ridiculous and touching, which André later recalled. She sniffed into her handkerchief, collected a clear little teardrop.

"I only wore that perfume for you, and now you detest me."

"But what's happening? What makes you say I don't love you, my darling?" was André's quick reaction.

"I am not your dar— . . ."

He kissed her with no resistance on her part.

"Of course I don't hate you. This perfume . . . you're so right to wear it. . . ."

"Particularly since you chose it for me."

He kissed her again.

"I'm a savage. Yes, a real savage. I was dreaming of going to the Argentine without a cent—to try to make good there for you."

"You're just crazy."

"And now I've forgotten to thank you for the book."

On their way down the stairs they noticed two small papers thumbtacked to the bulletin board. The first was a water-color on a sheet of rose-colored note paper. Stretched inside a heart was a little red-roofed house, geometrical and stylized in a childish way. A gay corkscrew of smoke came out of the tall chimney and there were curtains at the window. On each side of the house a little man pushed a loaded cart and two others carried sacks. Underneath was the caption:

"If your heart is not too hard, give to the works of Emmaus."

Madame Gilbert had done her best. With her ruler she had traced straight lines, the tiles of the roof, the bricks of the walls. Pinned under the sketch they saw the typewritten appeal advising that the ragpickers would be by to collect old clothes, scraps, paper, etc.

"What is it?" asked André, smiling.

That evening, after having read a chapter of a treatise on political economy entitled *Communism and Capitalism*, André tore the wrapper off of another book a friend had given him. The first thing he read was this passage:

> It is hard to imagine the number of people who, at the end of their resources, are dying in hiding, burrowed in filthy lairs waiting for death. . . . One would have to consult the police registers to check on figures and establish files. Just three lines in a paper under the "News in Brief" column, and then they're not all listed. A paralyzed woman, dying on a heap of litter, too feeble to call for help, chewed by rats, apprehensive, hearing them, seeing them, sensing their presence in terrifying proximity. Poor dying human beings, lonely, old, and unbelievably destitute, living in a décor of darkness, stench, and terror. . . . Suicides . . . found only when it is too late to save them, discovered simply by unexpected smells coming from under a door. . . . A tramp killed by the cold under his layers of sacks in the back of an empty lot, a stiff, bearded scarecrow from which it is impossible to turn one's look and memory. A mad musician dead from inanition and the effort to maintain his dignity, lying tucked neatly in bed near the rain pipes and geraniums in an attic. A plump blond girl murdered by her own hand with a knitting needle in a vain effort to cover up her error. . . .
> But in many of these horror-filled habitations people are not waiting for death. Young and old live in human foxholes or dark, airless, windowless rooms. Occasionally an opening is cut into the ceiling, but this gets filled by time and dust. In passing one of these dark rooms one might see a tiny seamstress huddled over her sewing in the light of the open door. These streets are crying

examples: *Rue Visconti, Rue des Hautes Formes, Passage de l'Avenir, Passage de la Trinité* . . .[1]

"Rue Visconti," thought André. "It's just two steps from where Jeanne lives, and she doesn't suspect anything of the sort. Even I cannot swear that two steps from where I am . . ."

He closed the book and turned out the light. But sleep did not come. Why this feeling, this torment, that neither his parents nor Jeanne would understand? What did he really want? He himself could not answer that. Was it just the taste for exotic adventure that had caused him to write to Argentina? Or was it the need to start from scratch, to prove his ability? Perhaps it was the desire to escape from a suffocating *security one had not deserved,* from the obscure remorse of owing nothing to oneself and all to one's wealthy family. Did he want to escape being engulfed by the egotism of this privileged circle and the obligation to stifle his tremendous need for justice and sacrifice? These dulled aspirations, must they, too, be considered "absurd"? Jeanne's words came back to him.

In the room the clinging fragrance of "Gypsy Laughter" hung heavily. He got up, threw his window open wide, and took in a deep breath of icy, cold air, just as if he were drinking water. But to the purity of the northern gale was added the smell of smoke and coal from the Aubervilliers factories. It was snowing in Paris, in the suburbs, on human shelters and on human shoulders.

[1] J. P. Clebert, *Paris Insolite.*

18: *The Dealers Come by*
A Case of Conscience

I sn't the Father with you?" asked Madame Gilbert, disappointed.

"He went off with another team," Filot told her, and after a glance around the attic added: "This will take two trips at least."

Madame Gilbert had put on overalls so that she could ferret into dusty corners she had never before visited. She was happy to discover all the things the former owner of the house had left under the eaves. Two folding beds, some broken-down chairs, an old, chipped bathtub, stacks of books, cases of fabric, old paintings.

"You'll be all dirty, Madame Gilbert."

She laughed. It excited her to open old trunks, pull out old clothes and newspapers dated 1925.

"I've never been up here before," she said. "My husband inherited the house three years ago. It's funny how alike all attics are. This is just like my parents' attic in Arles. I feel as if I were about to discover my grandmother's armchair. Oh, but look at this! Isn't this extraordinary?"

The four dealers joined her. In the back, on a large rafter which crossed the eaves, about a dozen stuffed birds were perched. A parrot with a blue and violet belly, his back gray with dust, was enthroned among smaller birds: jackdaws, wild ducks, a teal, a blackbird, a cuckoo, and a moor hen. The taxidermist had done his best to make them look like living birds; their beaks were open, their heads were caught in a startled attitude or were stretched as though the birds were in flight.

Perched on the beams were warblers, staring with glassy eyes at the four ragpickers and the little lady in white. Each jackdaw's single beady eye gleamed with a golden glint that contrasted with its black feathers.

"I remember now, my husband once mentioned he had an uncle who was fond of shooting. But the parrot?"

Lost in a brown study and wearing an expression of bitter irony under his heavy yellow beak, the large blue parrot seemed to float in the shadows. The electric bulb hanging in the attic doorway cast its light on the glistening feathers of his wings and breast.

"He couldn't have shot this parrot at Fontainebleau," said Madame Gilbert.

Slowly she stepped back, her enthusiasm fading. A feeling of discomfort and anguish had suddenly seized her. On one hand there was this evil-looking bird, on the other these sinister-looking men. Receding between the chairs, she said:

"Now, I'll let you get on with your work. All this belongs to you, and there's still more in the cellar. Come and tell me when you're through."

And she walked quickly back toward the light. . . .

"It's unbelievable all one can find," said Filot pensively.

"Well, let's go; first of all the heaviest—the bathtub."

"We'll have to see if the cart will stand up under it," said Lurson, the aristocrat. Denis and Gabi caught hold of the back legs.

"I expected it to be heavier," said Denis.

When the slow procession reached the second-floor landing, Mademoiselle Lucienne opened her door and said, "You'll come by, won't you? There are some things here for you."

"Yes," said Filot. "We're doing the apartments, too. We'll be back a little later, maybe this afternoon."

The attic cleared out, and the cart loaded within an inch of breaking its springs, there were still the bags to be filled.

Denis and Filot rang the door of the third-floor apartment. André answered the bell. Denis's youth surprised him. A boy his own age, so young—and a ragpicker.

"My parents are away," he said. "And there's nothing much in my room—maybe a couple of books."

"That's O.K. We'll come another day," said Denis. "Excuse us for bothering you."

"Wait; come in."

He opened the door to the man. Filot and Denis entered a luxurious hall, but there was nothing for the dealers in the student's little room. Its sole luxury was the reproduction of a Renoir, and a yellow-and-red cover for the bed. The wall at the end of the room was filled with rows of bookshelves.

"All I have is some port," said André.

"That's awfully nice of you, but we're in right much of a hurry."

André filled three glasses. He wanted to talk with Denis, find out how he got into this curious trade. He looked so young and delicate beside the other man whose face was swollen and badly shaven. Could they be father and son?

"Are you a ragpicker?"

"Yes," said Denis, smiling.

"Is that your trade, I mean?"

"That's everyone's trade, at Emmaus."

"But before?"

"Well, me," said Filot, after a moment's silence, "I owned a business in Madagascar."

"And I," said Denis, "I was a seminarist. I'm a volunteer rag-picker."

There was another silence.

"The others are waiting," said Filot finally.

Suddenly André went over to his bookcase and, opening his arms wide, caught up all the books from one shelf. Some of them fell, and Denis picked them up. He read their titles: *Chemical Components of Soap, Alcaloids Used in the Industry of Commercial Perfumes, What Is Productivity?* Then: *Man and His Destiny.*

"Does paper by weight interest you?"

"Everything interests us," said Filot. "As long as it'll bring in two cents. Emmaus lives from just that."

The books disappeared in the sack, landing at the bottom with an almost funereal sound.

"Come on. Spring cleaning. Help me," said the young man to Denis. "Second row."

"As long as you really don't need them any more . . ."

"One imagines one will need them until the day he dies. Take them."

Shaking hands with Filot and Denis as they left, he asked: "But what is all this Emmaus enterprise?"

With his free hand Filot reached in his inner coat pocket and handed the priest's tract to the young man.

"Here you are. Read it. So long, and thanks."

On the second-floor landing Mademoiselle Lucienne, who had been waiting for them to go by, opened her door. She held a little Second Empire clock decorated with a bronze statuette.

"Say there, how much will you give for this?"

Filot, bent low by his loaded sack, peered at her sideways.

"Nothing at all, Madame. We aren't buying."

A little before noon the spinster lady went up and knocked on André's door.

"Did the ragpickers call on you? They told me they weren't buying. You didn't *give* them your books, did you? How ridiculous!"

The young man smiled and shrugged his shoulders. "For years one thinks something is indispensable and then suddenly . . ." He handed her the tract. She read, nodding her head and murmuring from time to time:

"Of course, of course, I understand."

"They should be back again this afternoon."

"I'll see what I have that I don't need."

She went downstairs, not feeling quite herself. Her appetite had disappeared. She turned off her stove and looked around her apartment. She looked at it as if she were seeing it for the first time, as if every accessory forming the background of her life had suddenly acquired a very precious value and had now become threatened. There was her bed with its counterpane hand-embroidered by her mother; her marquetry writing desk cluttered with knickknacks, one of which was the little Second Empire clock decorated with an Angel of Silence; her library, with its six volumes of the Larousse encyclopedia, bought painstakingly by installments with her modest earnings as a college teacher; the carpet; her father's armchair with its leather cushion; a little Japanese vase and her reading lamp; the two paintings, one an original by an artist friend; her little radio; the gas stove . . . Then in her pint-sized kitchen all the indispensable utensils . . . indispensable . . . everything was indispensable! Most precious of all was the little gold crucifix set with five rubies affixed to the head of her bed.

A moment ago she had made up her mind to sell the little clock with the Angel, because after she paid her rent the fifteenth of January she knew she would run short of money. This happened from time to time. On several occasions she had tried to make some money out of the clock: she had offered it to a clockmaker and then to an antique dealer. Both had refused it: it was not even an original Second Empire piece, but a copy, dated 1900. A secondhand dealer had offered her such a laughable price that Mademoiselle Lucienne had put the clock back in its place on her desk. Though the works were still good, she no longer wound it, preferring a more practical alarm clock.

Her look caressed one by one the assortment of objects received from her parents or acquired through painful economies. All this was her property—her modest property, so indispensable to her comfort and security. These things with which she had lived for years, since childhood, seemed to protect her with their true friendship. No, in truth, there was nothing she could spare.

Her heart quiet, she got up and pushed the bolt on her door. The minute she did it, she felt a start of surprise.

"Why ever did I do that? I never bolt my door."

She shrugged her shoulders, feeling once again that vague uneasiness creeping up on her. Evidently the ragpickers' visit and the tract she had read had impressed her more than she cared to admit. She murmured to herself: "My dear girl, be your age. Dinnertime."

With difficulty she managed to swallow a bowl of bouillon. Incapable of eating any solid food, she made a cup of coffee. Then she started correcting her pupils' exercise books. She had a class from four to five.

Half anxious, as though she had been caught committing a crime, she mused: "Why did I bolt that door unless I was afraid the ragpickers would return? It's not so much that I fear these men. I don't. But I guess I'm a little ashamed of not having been charitable. No, I have nothing, nothing, just *nothing* to give them."

On her desk the little bronze Angel, his finger on his lips, looked more charming than ever. These things that belong to us, the sweetness and appeal they have—their power insidious, tyrannical.

Suddenly everything seemed to change. She went pale, as though nauseated. The tyranny of things! It is *they* that possess *you*, cling malignantly to you. They surround you with superstitious mania, impose on you an unhealthy taste for the past, the fear of living in poverty, the fear of renewing oneself in the future. Things inherited from the past force you to persevere in your mediocre way of life, a way of life woven of precarious comforts and short-term courage.

"Oh, my God, how miserable I am!" Standing up, Mademoiselle Lucienne tottered a bit, giddy and disgusted at the hold these things had had on her for so many years. She prayed God for strength to deny herself, to begin a virgin existence, a life of joy, strength, and fervor in poverty.

Nothing to give? Why, everything—all that! And her look wandered in a kind of horror to the Angel on the clock, the marquetry desk, the cross set with rubies, the cushion, the carpet, the coalbin, all things which could serve others. The words of the soul-disturbing tract kept running through her mind:

> *Everyone who can . . . give now, today, every day, all you can give.*
> *Give because tonight babies are crying.*
> *Give because homes are being broken up by poverty.*

She passed her hand across her forehead, moist with perspiration. And she stopped struggling. Suddenly there was no problem, there was only the peace that comes from above.

The Father gazed at the gold crucifix set with five rubies which Filot had just handed him.

"Stamped fourteen carats, Father. If the stones are real, it's worth at least 10,000 francs."

"Twenty-five square meters of secondhand tin sheeting; that will be a roof for the Raymonds'," said the Father with a sigh.

19: *Everyday Problems*
The Compote Dish

I N H E R office Mademoiselle was totaling the number of Emmaus inhabitants as of February 12.

"Twenty-six, twenty-seven, twenty-eight, twenty-nine, counting the widower who arrived last night. Figures have almost
doubled in the last month. If we go on like this, Father, we'll
never last."

"Just have to," murmured the latter, busy with his incoming
mail.

A letter from the electric company informed him that if
the bills were not paid by return mail, they would be obliged
to . . .

Outdoors, snow flurries mingled with bursts of sunshine. A
truck came slowly up the street, turned into the gate, and entered
the court, one wheel crushing the edge of the flower beds.

"At last, there's Carol. He pays cash," said the priest with a
note of relief in his voice. Carol was the wholesale dealer.

"It's about time he cleared out all the junk from the first floor.
And the cellar's full, too."

The priest went down to greet the secondhand dealer, Emmaus's best client. Mademoiselle plunged once more into her
accounts, searching for the inextricable balance.

Ten minutes later the telephone rang. A woman's voice said:

"I'm a friend of Madame Gilbert. She spoke to me of the
Father, of his admirable work. I have something for him."

"Would you let us have your address, please?"

"Avenue Daumesnil. Could the Father call in the afternoon? I would like very much to meet him."

"The Father won't be able to come himself this afternoon but we'll be sure to send some of our men."

"But I wouldn't dream of giving them to just anyone."

"But you can trust them, Madame."

It was worth sending the second team with a pushcart at once. The first team, in the recently purchased Renault, was on its way to Montrouge to collect a stack of used tires. Filot had left for the Flea Market in a smaller car acquired in January. These two secondhand cars, both in constant use, were no longer sufficient to cover the needs of the house. But for the moment it was impossible to buy anything, even on terms. First the current debts had to be settled, then building materials and food had to be purchased. The profit earned by the resale of used merchandise was not sufficient to patch up the deficit. Once again, and as always, they were living from day to day like tightrope walkers.

Luckily Carol was going to pay for the merchandise he had purchased two weeks ago. Mademoiselle took her shawl and proceeded downstairs with the address of the lady living on Avenue Daumesnil. A flurry of snow and rain blew around the corner of the house. Sheltered by the truck, the Father was arguing with the wholesale dealer whose men were hauling the merchandise from the cellar.

"Copper, zinc, and nonmetals have dropped in price, Monsieur l'Abbé, what with the American imports coming in now. Look. Read yesterday's stock-market quotations."

With difficulty he opened his paper in the wind and rain. Mademoiselle skirted a heap of unsorted iron and made her way to the wrecking shop. The shed had been finished just fifteen days before. Under the eaves hung the big blue parrot. He could not have found a better place.

"That must be Bobi's idea," thought Mademoiselle.

It was warm in the workshop. Philippe and Bobi were dismantling unmendable, unsalable objects. Separately, into five different barrels, they threw pieces of iron, tin, copper, lead, and "miscellaneous" metals. Combustible materials, such as wood, leather, and plastic, were tossed into a wooden box. Scrap pieces of stone, marble, and porcelain went into still another box.

An old man who had arrived the night before was seated by the stove rolling himself a cigarette. He rose awkwardly as Mademoiselle entered.

An assortment of objects was heaped on the ground, the workbenches, and shelves. There were twisted pipes, oil lamps, copper pans, chimneypieces, motorcycle motors, and everything else that the repair squad had salvaged from the incessant stream of merchandise that had poured in during the past month.

On the wall hung a bugle, its pipe perforated by a bullet. Bobi, the ex-Verdun veteran, did not have the heart to demolish this relic which had come to join him here. Just as with the men, each object had made the journey to Emmaus in its last stage of decrepitude, and each one had a personal story to tell, perhaps a long and mysterious story that no longer interested anyone. Tools or knickknacks which had passed through so many hands, had played their part in scenes of love or violence, had been admired or finally served their purpose, all came to an end here with Bobi's hammer or Philippe's saw. And then, reincarnated, they started their return trip to the world, to unknown destinies —to serve new masters.

"You're not going to break this up, are you?" asked Mademoiselle, touching the bronze Angel's head that topped Mademoiselle Lucienne's little clock.

"The key is lost," said Bobi. "Filot doesn't want it for the Flea Market. He says the weight of the bronze is worth more than the clock. It weighs about two kilos."

Old Bobi spoke with a lisp and sometimes shot out a thin stream of saliva. His mutilated lower jaw, shot off by a piece of shrapnel, gave him a face like a rabbit. From under the scraggy mustache of his half-open mouth jutted a large black tooth. But above all this hideousness there were two candid blue eyes, soft and serene.

Like Philippe, he was a professional scavenger. A bachelor of arts, he was still fond of reading and philosophizing.

Mademoiselle was stroking the smooth round head of the statue.

"What a pity," she murmured.

"That's what we say every time, Mademoiselle. But the main thing is we should get as much out of it as we can. You can be sure it sometimes hurts me to wreck gimmicks like that—specially when I think the bronze may be used again for making bullets."

"I'm going to take it along. Maybe it would make someone at Clos Fleuri very happy." Then Mademoiselle handed Philippe the paper with the address of the lady on Avenue Daumesnil.

"It should be interesting," she said. "A friend of Madame Gilbert."

"I remember," said Philippe. "I'll take two men along. It's ten o'clock now. We'll need two or three hours to cross the Vincennes wood with the pushcart. Maybe the lady will give us something to eat or drink. I'll take Dédé and Kurt with me."

"No," said Mademoiselle. "Kurt's papers aren't in order. Take Léon."

When she returned to the office the Father was talking to Djibouti, now promoted to chief of the building lot. Bending over the Clos Fleuri plan, they were studying the water and plumbing systems.

"The problem lies in getting the water out, not in bringing it in," the priest was saying. "Clos Fleuri lies in a bowl. To drain it from there into the Marne we would have to cross the railroad embankment. I've talked it over with an engineer. He says the work would come to at least 2,000,000 francs. Well, we'll have to dig septic tanks."

Djibouti shook his head.

"O.K. Let's forget it then. How far along are you now?"

"We're putting electricity in at the Martinets'. And the others are finishing the road."

"Were the scouts able to help you last Saturday?"

"Sure, sure. We mustn't discourage them."

"The Marchands' house will be ready the day after tomorrow. Can we get rid of the gypsy wagon?"

"Yes, the Sansennes have priority on it. The grandfather has developed rheumatism from living a month in the tent with all this rain."

Automatically both men turned to the window. The sky had darkened, and the great heavy clouds seemed barely to skirt the rooftops. It suddenly became so dark that Mademoiselle, who was typing, was forced to turn on a light.

"Now that I come to think of it," said the priest, "they offered me a good buy on the framework of a bus that used to transport officers between Paris and Villacoublay. It's built like a plane body of strips of wood and light canvas."

"For the Farisa's."

"Sure."

Again they bent over the plans. The priest erased the word "tent" from the lots 14 and 18, and marked "gypsy wagon" and "autobus." On the Marchands' lot he erased the "gypsy wagon" and sketched a little house. Eight similar sketches occupied their numbered places. This childlike drawing gave the impression of a game, of an advance of pieces on a chessboard. Eight houses against twelve tents, gypsy wagons, and bus hulks. The game was not won yet. So many families were still expecting a roof. Djibouti started for the door.

"The contractors have left a pile of trash along the road bank that's gotta be cleared away."

"Yes," said the Father. "Plaster remnants."

"Not only that. There's also metal, pieces of tin, pipe, and some boards that we can do something with."

"Fine. Take the cart."

Mademoiselle turned round.

"It's just gone out with Philippe to pick up some secondhand things."

The sound of singing came from the street. It was a chorus of young boys, singing a marching song:

> "March on, keep step, do not lag,
> The road's your best friend, my lad."

With the sound of marching feet there also came the hammering of hail on the road. The singing stopped and the troop of scouts quickened their steps and marched into the court. There they dispersed, shouting and laughing. A few of the boys ran for cover under the eaves of the refectory.

The majority of the group made for the inn. Left alone in the court under the hard beating of the hail, their chief, a tall youth wearing shorts, shouted:

"Troop St. Louis! I never told you to break ranks."

Then he shrugged his shoulders, and followed by a dancing halo of white dust he stoically crossed the Flowered Cloister.

Djibouti turned from the door to the Father.

"I forgot to mention the wallpaper for the Marchand house. She's picked what she wants and we need eight rolls at . . ."

The priest interrupted:

"Can she pay for the paper herself? It's quite impossible for us to advance one cent."

His voice was clipped and the tone surprisingly sharp.

Djibouti was silent for a moment.

"O.K. She can wait then. It's not as important as all that."

The Father then said in softer tones:

"It is important, though. Wallpaper is an insulator. And in this weather . . . with the kids . . . I'll talk to the painter. We owe him money anyway."

Then he turned to the secretary.

"I just made 23,000 francs with the secondhand dealer. I had hoped for at least 35,000, but we must send some money anyway to the electric company. Since December they've been threatening to cut off the current, and since we can't do without gas either . . . Really there's only one way I can see of cutting down—that's on food. Otherwise, I'll have to send some of our friends away. There are too many of us now, and . . ."

The telephone rang. Mademoiselle picked up the receiver.

"Father, it's for you. A worker-priest."

"Yes, hello, François."

He raised his hand, signaling Djibouti to wait.

Then he listened attentively.

"I'll see what I can do, François. Send them to me. Good-by, François, and thanks."

"Dear me," he sighed, hanging up the receiver. "A family of six. Evicted squatters. They've been living this past week in a deserted house. They notified the proprietor they were there but he didn't send a reply. Last night he sent the police."

"We still have two empty tents," said Djibouti.

"All right. Pitch them at Clos Fleuri on lot 19, side by side."

"I'll have to wait till a car gets back," said Djibouti. "The Renault should be in any minute now."

The Father took up his cape. "Come with me and let's check what's left in the stockroom in the way of blankets. There should still be one good stove."

Twenty minutes later the telephone rang again.
"Emmaus?"
A woman's voice, clear, slightly affected, drawing out the last syllable, asked to speak to the Father.
"The Father is busy right now," said the secretary. "Can I give him a message?"
A moment's hesitation. Then:
"I have, Madame, an armchair for him. An armchair which I don't need."
"If you wish to give me your address, our team will stop by one day soon."
"I want to get rid of it today. And I don't want to give it up to anyone but the Father. You understand, it's a good chair, but it's in my way."
"I understand perfectly well, Madame, but the Father . . ."
From the street a rumble reached her ears, grew strong, shaking the air like the thunder of a giant airplane. The windows rattled. Mademoiselle could not hear the voice on the telephone. She raised her own voice.
"The Father is busy getting a new family settled."
The old Renault gave the full of its tired ten horsepower, and panting, made the hill with its cargo of used tires. Turning to cross the drive, the motor sputtered, spit two salvos, then roared full steam up the incline. The noise traveled across the room and the windowpanes on the opposite side joined in the game; and still through the telephone came the dry, obstinate voice like that of a somnambulist:
"I know that what the Father is doing is wonderful, very touching, but this armchair must go now. It's taking up too much room."
"I'm sorry, Madame, but it's really impossible to get it today. I'm afraid you'll have to take it or leave it. We consider that getting a homeless family settled is more important at the moment than getting an armchair."
"It's now or never."

Clack. Mademoiselle hung up and closed her eyes. The noise had subsided. Silence, a great peace, a pure void, which for a moment nothing interrupted.

Then the echo of the voice sounded in Mademoiselle's ears and reminded her of the day's first telephone call, the lady from Avenue Daumesnil, where the men had gone with the pushcart.

"Let's hope she'll give the poor things something to eat. They have at least a two-hour march to get there," she mused.

Philippe, young Dédé, and Léon, a good friend who had arrived at the beginning of the week, were crossing the Vincennes wood under the hail, pushing the cart before them. Its springs were broken.

A little before noon they came to the Avenue Daumesnil address. They were soaked, sweating, and puffing. It was a fine house, with a balcony and balustrade. The harvest would surely be good. The generous lady would surely understand. She would certainly offer them something to eat or drink.

Up to the third floor. The little maid looked them up and down.

"We're here for what the lady promised us."

She opened large, suspicious eyes. No one had told her anything. Leaving the men standing in the entrance, she hurried on to warn her mistress.

"Not bad, hum?" whispered Léon. "It looks pretty good."

"Behave, now, you're in society."

The maid returned and asked them to wait a moment.

They waited for twenty minutes at the entrance, shaking with cold in their wet clothes.

Then the lady suddenly appeared before them, gay, well-dressed, fresh-looking, perfumed. She was about forty and disconcertingly dynamic.

"Oh, yes," she cried. "I had almost forgotten about you. I have something for Monsieur l'Abbé. My friend, Madame Gilbert, told me. What a wonderful man! Oh, I know all he does, true Christian charity. . . . How beautiful it is, to go and find the tramps, beggars, outcasts. . . . I work with charities myself."

As the lady started impetuously talking, the boys from Emmaus first smiled politely. Then Philippe frowned. Tramps. . . . O.K. He had been a tramp once, but it displeased him that people should forget that he was now respectable and a worker.

And then the Abbé was not Monsieur l'Abbé, he was the Father, their Father. Those who called him Monsieur l'Abbé belonged to a different race. The ladies who talked of charity and charitable works in that tone were also of a different race from those who, on occasion, benefited from that "charity." They were the elite for whom charity was just a supplementary luxury. They never lived with the poor, never risked their lives, and did not compromise themselves in any way with the poor. "But let her talk," thought Philippe. "Let her talk . . . we'll get to the end sometime, and then get down to serious business."

Twelve-thirty chimed and the lady was still chattering.

The men would have liked to have gotten started, but "the bourgeois are talkers"; they talk fast and so well, and they know so much. Listening to them you might think they know everything. The lady was telling of her misfortunes during the war.

"I, too, have suffered much. I know what it means."

Suddenly she interrupted herself:

"But you must be hungry. Wait a minute."

She quickly left the lovely room. The men looked at each other, smiled. It will be well-earned, this snack.

She reappeared carrying high and very carefully a porcelain compote.

"There!" she cried triumphantly. "This is what I had promised you. Real Limoges porcelain. It's a little chipped. But you'll still get a good price for it."

On the street Dédé was all for smashing it into smithereens. An old chipped dish, worth nothing, and for which they had wasted their entire morning.

"Let's keep it as a souvenir," said Philippe. "It's well worth it."

So they left, their stomachs empty—as empty as their little cart.

20: *Emmaus Faces New Problems*
Bobi's Idea

I N T H E early hours of this same February afternoon the leader
of the scout troop went up to the Father who had just come
out onto the porch.

"We are about to start working on your lot at Clos Fleuri,"
he said.

The sun was shining intermittently but there was an icy wind.
The scouts were assembled in marching order in the yard. A flag
fluttered at the head of each of the three patrols. The youngsters'
eyes were fixed on the Father. Their bare knees were shaking
with cold.

"Yes, and I thank you, but I'm afraid there won't be very
much to do," the priest told them.

"Youngsters of good will can always find something to do,"
said the scout leader, raising his voice so that the boys would
hear.

"Then perhaps they can help our men clear the debris left
over from the building. There's a heap of scrap tin, iron, and
wood in the ditch along the embankment."

"That's what I mean, Father. Thank you. The boys must
understand. That will make a wonderful good deed for the day."

The priest smiled and thought:

"Charity . . . it's entirely different from a 'good deed.' But
why disappoint them? Why explain that a 'good deed,' praise-

worthy, to be sure, seems more like personal hygiene than a true service rendered to a brother in distress? It only makes sense if our constant deep need for sacrifice is on the alert. These children's help will lighten Djibouti's task and let him concentrate on other work—getting the new families settled. That now seems to be the main thing."

The scout leader, turning to his troop, called them to attention. "Scouts, always . . ."

"Ready!" answered the twenty unmatched voices.

"Repeat: Scouts, always . . ."

"Ready!"

At the stroke of four a young man knocked on the office door. He had a straightforward look, a well-shaven face, he wore a comfortable overcoat. He said he was a student and interested in questions of social welfare. He wanted to convince himself in practice, through personal observation, of the workability of a communal enterprise like Emmaus, controlled neither by state nor capitalistic interests.

"Emmaus is a commercial enterprise," said the Father. "But not only that . . ."

"I know," answered the youth.

Then after a silence: "I saw your circular; I think I understand."

"If you are only interested in the study of our organization, it's very simple and I can explain it to you. Salvage and construction. The homeless who have found homes here help to build houses for other homeless ones."

"Father, to go still deeper into this, I would like to work with you. Very frankly, I feel the need of an experience such as this."

The Father made a mental note of the boy's timidity, and reflected for a moment. The youth had arrived on the very day he had made up his mind that he would have to reduce either workers in the community or economize on food.

"It's going to be extremely hard for me to keep you. Our situation is very, very uncertain."

But the visitor insisted, said he would work for nothing, and if necessary would pay for his meals as a boarder.

Within himself the priest was once again amazed at the emotion, the admiration, that those who came to Emmaus felt once they penetrated into the true spirit of the community. This secret need of devotion, latent in every man, sometimes lies dormant, but then again it sometimes gets translated into action. How uplifting this was, but how careful one had to be of too much enthusiasm! Only service over a long period, like that of Denis, gave authenticity to the person's sincerity.

"I'm going to come stay with you for six months," said André.

Bobi lit the lamp of the wrecking shed.

"Feeling better?" he said to Philippe, who, huddled close to the stove, was shaking and unable to get warm after his trip in the rain from Avenue Daumesnil. "I'll get you some wine from the kitchen. That'll warm you up and do you good."

Philippe sat in silence. He felt so tired, and when he breathed he felt oppressed. When he coughed, the cough did not seem to relieve him. Sickness. That was the only thing they had brought back with them that day. That and the chipped compote. Bobi came back empty-handed, and in a voice announcing catastrophe:

"There's no more wine. Alexandre wasn't kidding. There'll be no wine for dinner tonight either. Damn it all! Things are really going to pot. Give me thirty francs. I'm off to the café. If I see the Father I'll explain."

Philippe shrugged his aching shoulders and rummaged in his pockets. Just as he did he heard sounds of singing.

"Once there was a little cart—pull, boys, pull . . ."

The young, changing voices which seemed to come from near the heap of iron by the workshop suddenly fell silent.

"Empty all that"—the Father's voice.

Bobi stepped out on the porch. The scouts had turned the cart upside down, spilling their load of scrap metal, wood, and old cement sacks at the foot of the already good-sized pyramid.

"You see, Bobi," said the Father, entering the circle of light in the workshop. "These kids have turned into ragpickers just like us."

"Where did they get all that?" said Bobi.

"From Clos Fleuri. That's what was left on the building lot."

He turned to the scouts.

"Thanks. You're a swell lot of youngsters and this really is a good deed. Leave the cart here—the men will put it away."

"Good-by, Father."

The boys left talking, laughing, happy with their day's work. Bobi shrugged his shoulders.

"Do you know what they've been doing, Father, those kids?"

"They've been collecting secondhand things."

"No, Father, they've been ragpicking on trash piles. They tell me that junk dealing doesn't bring enough. I can show you places where every day we could collect twenty times this without racking our brains a bit. It's all right on the city dumps."

Near the stove Philippe started to cough in long, deep fits. The bell rang for supper.

". . . Ragpicking on trash piles, Father," mused Bobi as they walked out the door.

In the refectory, after the meal, the priest rose from the table and spoke.

"One moment, please. I have something to say."

The men near the door stopped on their way out. Their mournful voices dropped. A cheerless meal—soup, cheese, and no wine.

Standing between the two back tables, the Father, just as he was about to start speaking, recalled that just last December 29 he had been about to make the same declaration that today could no longer be postponed.

On that day he had been thinking of putting off the announcement until the next day when Philippe came to him with the offer to scavenge in the trash cans. This provisionally had saved Emmaus. Today they were back again at almost the same point.

The thirty men, most of whom had kept on their caps, were looking at him with anxious expressions. The fixed stares of those eyes, shaded by their peaked caps . . . they were all hungry. Doing without wine, particularly, seemed hard to these Frenchmen.

"You all know," said the Father, "that the profit of our work is the comrade who enters to join us; our work should bring in enough to enable us to receive an extra man. But now we're making no profit because there are too many of us. Secondhand dealing does not bring in enough to feed thirty men. Today we have a new friend. Yesterday two; five in all this week. Despite the pains each of you are taking, we cannot collect more with only two cars and a little cart. The construction at Clos Fleuri doubles our expenses."

Some of the men bowed their heads. They seemed to say: "No use talking any more. We know what this means."

"So this is where we stand. We either have to send away the newcomers and accept no more, or we all stay together and eat soup and cheese, with no wine. It's up to you to decide. It's diffi-cult to give up some things, particularly since our trade is not an easy one."

Léon went pale. Having only arrived the night before, he risked being first on the list.

Two brothers, Spanish refugees, working at Emmaus for the last three days and understanding practically no French, ex-changed a few words with each other in their native tongue. In the stillness which had immobilized most of the men the old man who worked in the wrecking shed with Bobi stood up and, shuffling out, said:

"Off to Nanterre."

"Wait a minute," said the Father.

The other shrugged his shoulders without even turning.

"What for? I've had it."

And he left.

Another late arrival watched him go and then turned his eyes away.

"It's up to you all," repeated the Father.

"We'll all stay," growled a voice.

The Father detained Bobi and made him sit down next to him.

"What was this you were saying about ragpicking on the city dumps?"

21: *Ragpicking on the Dumps*

I T II A D been raining for two days. But toward evening several patches of sky cleared up and a rainbow appeared across the plain. The dump had become a black mire of mud. Now the men had to wade into this sea and clear away the slime in order to get to the garbage which was still cemented together by frost. Deeper down was a kingdom of decay and crawling things.

The delegation of scavengers advanced slowly along the clay-covered road with banks nearly ten feet high. Beyond the warehouse they saw a man near a gypsy wagon, a solitary figure who was working the dump on his own. The men from Emmaus watched his small dark silhouette repeat the motion: bend down, stand up, carry the sack to the edge of the road. In appreciating the efforts of this solitary man, they suddenly realized the force of their own community.

Directed by Bobi, the six Emmaus apprentices explored the vein of garbage with short, probing jabs of their hooks, forks, or their hands. Here they gleaned riches that would mean life for the community: paper, rags, iron, shoes, bones, tin cans. They stuffed their findings into a sack or tossed them into three large iron bins with a resounding clang that shook the rainy silence.

They had started this work the night before. This evening the truck would bring tents for those who were to settle on the lot for the duration of the job. This was a rough assignment, but the six men had all volunteered to do it.

To André it all seemed a dream, but he had wanted to live

such a dream. He had dreamed of clearing virgin forests in the Argentine. Now here was practically the same adventure, barely fifteen miles from Paris. Wearing a bowler and a waterproof square of canvas thrown across his shoulders, he was dragging treasure from the mud. By his side his comrades were doing the same elementary task. Wind, rain, space . . . and peace within him. He had dreamed of giving up his job—work that seemed too easy and absurd. Here the only absurdity was circumstance, and this setting in which he could never have pictured himself before. But the point of the work itself was concise and clear. This filthy rag would be washed tonight, sold tomorrow, and finally would help feed Emmaus.

Coming out of his daydream, he looked at Lurson. This aristocratic gentleman had not yet conquered his repugnance and made a face as he worked with gloves on. Actually, the odor of the dump was not so bad, not nearly so strong as in summer when flies swarmed above and worms crawled beneath. Occasionally, though, when the fork hooked out a package of garbage, the stench lying dormant underneath would awaken, hit one in the face, and disappear, carried away by the wind. Then Lurson would set his black-bearded jaw and grimace again. André smiled. He remembered the delicious "Gypsy Laughter" perfume. Once more he said to himself that all this would be cleaned, washed, sorted, and would again be raw material for industry, and that would mean money and bread for Emmaus. It was a case of turning manure into bread.

Old Bobi dragged himself upright. His back ached. He wiped his hands on his coat and lit a cigarette. The aroma of tobacco affected the workers as if someone had cried: "Stop." It awakened them from their active trance. They stood up, looked at each other.

"Good! We're not in pieces yet," said Patoche, the one who had been rescued from drowning.

André would have liked to reply: "This is the point: we are in pieces." But he restrained himself. The men were volunteers, they knew that the salvation of Emmaus depended on every recuperated piece.

"Hey there, you loafer, look what you're leaving behind you," said Bobi to Lurson, giving a poke with his fork into a ball of horsehair that resembled a human head of hair. The heap of hair stuck fast in the dark mud, resisting his pull, until suddenly a part came off dripping with mud like a bleeding scalp.

"Excuse me," murmured Lurson. He turned his back on his comrades; weaving dizzily, he went a dozen steps toward the edge of the slope and vomited.

Bobi shrugged his shoulders.

"No guts! Should have seen what I found one day out on the Villecresnes dump. A newborn baby, half rotted. That didn't make me sick. That's life. Imagine you're a gold digger and that you may find some treasure in this muck. Like a ragpicker friend of mine one day found a soapbox full of tin cans that were real heavy; so he opened one: *gold*. Poured gold in every can. He reported it. A year later it was all his. Today he's a millionaire, driving big American cars, believe it or not."

André smiled. True or not, this story picked up the spirits of the team. After all, it was possible. Everything was possible. A thousand daily adventures of Paris and her suburbs were deposited here in terrifying remnants and unusual relics. Here, even more than in the attics where the dealers go to look for them, inanimate objects come to the end of their existence. This is their rendezvous with nothingness, a great cemetery of Things. And from this nothingness can still be drawn resources of Life. André, suddenly filled with a great realization of strength and joy, stood up. This was what he had wanted, to arrive at this feeling. In a surge of friendship he observed his companions: Old Bobi, Patoche, the attempted suicide, the two taciturn Spanish brothers, and Lurson, the "aristocrat," who had bravely taken up his work again. André respected them. Then he thought of his father with his successful perfume business, of their beautiful home, of their two villas, of their cars. None of that belonged to him any more. What he had wanted in coming to Emmaus was to find himself alone and naked among men truly and equally bared.

"You are a snob," his fiancée had told him. His heart twinged and, picking up his hook, he started poking in the mud, trying to chase away the bitterness and anguish he felt welling up inside him. Jeanne and this misunderstanding between them. . . . Why couldn't she understand that this apprenticeship with the ragpickers was as necessary to him as a cure for alcoholism? He needed the truth. He needed to meet real men, to live with them, to find his own strength in theirs. "But then," she had said, "haven't you enough strength of your own? Aren't you ashamed of begging for strength from outcasts and tramps?" Of course it was impossible to explain to her what was still so obscure to himself. Only men like the priest or like young Denis could understand. To end the argument, Jeanne had said, "You relish decadence." To which André had smiled, declining to defend himself any longer. "Yes, perhaps."

They ate on the job. That evening three trucks of public street cleaners poured out their loads near the gypsy wagon.

The Emmaus group ceased working to watch.

"What the——" growled Bobi. "Here we are scratching in mud that has already been gone through. We should go over there and take a poke at the new load."

"Yes, but this is the corner we were told we could use by the chief of the unloading lot," said André.

The man in charge of the dump—the intermediary between the street cleaners and the owners of the land—had divided the different lots among the ragpickers. His black Peugeot was seen approaching now, following the last truck.

"Let's go," said Bobi.

"Why not?" thought André. "We could talk to him. Our corner is the worst on the lot."

They started off, wading through pools, stumbling into the deep ruts made by heavy trucks. Two trucks had already left.

The last one backed onto the edge of the field. The hoist raised slowly and the junk poured onto the ground. The crewmen in the truck caught hold of a piece as it went by. Their looks darkened as the men from Emmaus approached. The man in charge, wearing high leather boots and a soft felt hat, was talking to the truck driver and smoking.

"M'sieur Robert," Bobi spoke up, "our corner over there is not too good."

"You're newcomers to this field."

"What do they want?" cried another ragpicker.

"You settle the question with Fernandel," said the disposal chief. "I gave him this lot. He works with the trucking team."

"Fernandel," professional ragpicker and owner of the gypsy wagon, was a big man whose coat was somewhat short and showed his tattooed body. His face recalled that of the famous French actor, sad, long, and drawn out, but his teeth were black and unpleasant to look at.

He came toward the group, his hook in his hands.

"Let them go to——!" he said in a deep voice.

The three men from the truck followed close by. André thought of the expression currently in use, "Fighting like ragpickers." For the priest's sake this must be avoided.

So he said, "Our lot has already been cleared by the truck guys and the ragpickers. There isn't much of anything left!"

"So what?" said one of the men from the truck. "You want to be served on a silver platter?"

"When I tell you this," said André, "it's not for me. I'm not working for myself."

"Working for the Pope, I suppose?"

"We are trying to organize a community where we can live."

"Who is your boss?"

"A priest."

The other jeered.

"A priest. No kidding," Bobi said. "It's true—the priest who was deputy . . ."

"A priest who was a *deputy!*" said Fernandel. "It gets better and better."

"Priests are not members of Parliament, and anyway they couldn't care less about ragpickers, no kidding."

"Wait a minute," broke in the disposal chief. "It's true. Their priest asked me for a lot."

"Great Scott," cried Fernandel. "If the priests get into this act we're lost."

"Don't let him talk you into it!" said one of the truckers.

"This dump is ours," said Fernandel. "And when I see your priest I'll cure him from ever wanting to come into our ground again."

"I don't insist," said André. "We'll go."

"You're a fine one," growled Bobi.

Near him the two Spaniards, their eyes glowing, were tightly holding on to their forks.

"We'll go," repeated André.

"Back to the manure pile," said Bobi. "While here . . ." and he made a step toward the heap of easily recoverable treasures.

"Get the hell out of here!" shouted Fernandel. "Or else you'll see what you get."

Suddenly from the road came the sound of a car's horn. André recognized the silhouette of the old Renault.

"Why, there's the Father!" he said with relief.

The Father and Djibouti got out of the car.

"Well, I'll be damned," said Fernandel. "Believe it or not— a priest."

Speechless, he looked at the worn windbreaker, the shabby cassock, the old beret, and the bearded face.

"*Bonjour,*" said the Father with a smile. "We just couldn't get here earlier." He turned to André.

"I have brought the tent along."

The men fell silent.

The priest's eyes scanned every face. He stretched out his hand to the man in charge of the dump and to Fernandel and his comrades, who gave him theirs after a moment's hesitation. They saw it was the hand of a workman.

"I was just asking them," said Bobi, "about letting us work here, where the pickings are a little better."

Listening to him, the Father was studying Fernandel's tattooed body.

"You have a wonderful tattoo there," he said.

The man opened his coat, revealing the head of Christ. Underneath were these words: "He has suffered." Above were the words: "So have I!"

"It's beautiful," said the priest gravely. "Where did you get that done?"

"Out there, when I was in stir."

"We'll come to an agreement," said the Father knowingly.

"Fine with me," said Fernandel, with a broad grin that showed his large, decayed teeth.

22: *The Flea Market*
The Epileptic

T HIS was quite a day for Filot.
Stoically he stood shivering in the cold wind that swept
the traffic circle at Porte de Montreuil. He had spread out his
merchandise at the edge of the grassy square between the high
new buildings.

The Flea Market was almost deserted that morning. At the
other end of the grass plot there were six benches sheltered by
a canvas awning. Emmaus could not yet afford a stall, so the
gleanings of their *chine* dealing lay heaped on the grass: a
wooden rocking horse, a scooter, two air guns, a child's tricycle, a
checkerboard minus the men, a little box whose precious marquetry was chipped, an old phonograph with five records, a "real
marble" bust of Venus, a little table dated 1900, two coat hang-
ers, an old stamp album with half of the stamps torn out, enamel
jugs, basins, picture frames, two pairs of roller skates, trunks.
There were five large wicker baskets, and among all these objects Filot, himself, might have just been a wax figure for sale.

The truck would come back for him later in the evening. A
cigarette in his mouth, hands in his pockets, he stood glued to
one spot waiting for the eventual client. The day started off
poorly. Blue with cold, the passers-by hurried along without
stopping, housewives from the district, some old loafers who, to

kill time, touched everything and bought nothing. There were few collectors. At noon the children would be out of school and men would come by from work. That Saturday morning the priest had told Filot he needed 5,000 francs in order to pay the ragpickers their 200-franc Sunday dole. And 5,000 francs are not so easily made from selling unwanted merchandise at the Flea Market.

But it could happen. The market is unpredictable, as full of surprises as a shooting gallery. The game is bewildering, the psychology of an amateur antique collector being very different from that of an ordinary shopper. Along the boulevards one sees idlers who want nothing more than to be entertained and amused by the eloquence and tricks of the hawker. The gimmick the latter is offering may not be indispensable but it's new, amusing, cheap, and one always has a bit of money to waste. But at the Flea Market the clients are made up of the display man from an amateur theater group, an antique dealer from Paris, a private collector and, in summer, visiting Americans who swarm to the famous market in quest of Paris souvenirs. However, the game is generally played between the poor themselves. What prudence, what suspicion, and what hesitation before they will bring themselves to ask for a price!

For over ten minutes an old gentleman, doubtless retired, had been examining the phonograph. With his finger he had checked the needle, the sound box, and was now carefully reading the titles of the records. Filot lit another cigarette, half closing his eyes. Don't intervene. Don't interrupt the study prematurely, or else the potential client will take flight in fear of having his arm twisted. One must allow him to think he has made a find, a windfall. But be careful . . . never let the moment come when his interest may wane. Filot shook himself out of his torpor.

"The works are good," he said. "It's a real bargain."

"Could I play a record?" the old man inquired timidly.

"The Boys of the Navy." The wax was dull and scratched, but this was the only record that was not cracked. Filot had tried it at Emmaus. A squeaky band played a few bars and then a chorus of men's voices broke out with gusto, but so indistinctly and distant that they seemed to emanate from the wicker trunk on which the phonograph was perched.

"From the South Pole to the North
In every little port
There's more than one blonde . . ."

The old man bent his head. He smiled a toothless smile. A young couple, a housewife, and two schoolboys stopped to survey this happy heap of junk.

Business looked good at last.

"How much?"

"Three hundred francs including the records."

The old man tried to bargain. Two hundred and fifty francs. It was a gift for his sister-in-law. He was not rich. All he had was his modest pension. Filot was not impressed by sentiment. Life was not made up of sentiment. Be strong, take the risk, make the other give in, impose your price, and refuse to bargain. The old man gave in.

This little victory filled Filot with bitter pride, reminding him of the days when as a successful businessman he had dealt in millions. As owner of a large warehouse at Tamatave he employed fifty natives. But in 1938 he caught fever and had to come back north. He put all his savings into building a magnificent villa near Lille. Two years later France was invaded. His house was looted and burned. At forty-five Filot could not start out again to seek a fortune. The state had given him a laughable pension. Little by little he had fallen into a state of apathy, doing odd jobs here and there, finally working as an accountant. Eventually he lost that job and from then on lived by his wits from day to day. Last December, on the advice of a man he had met out in the Colonies, he came to Emmaus. Now, in the cold March wind on this wide crossroads, Filot was dreaming again of spending his last days in Madagascar. But this dream was still not strong enough to shake him from his apathy. He was penniless. And even if he succeeded in leaving, he knew that the jobless were numerous out there.

"How much for the roller skates, M'sieur?"

"One hundred francs."

The two schoolboys re-counted their fortune.

"All we have is ninety francs."

"That's too bad, isn't it?"

Filot was not defending his own interests. He had no more personal desires at all. The men at Emmaus did not interest him personally either. Could he claim a friend among them? Djibouti, maybe. But he had the interest of Emmaus at heart. It was the whole house, from the priest down to the young hot-bloods, that he must defend. On his Place de Montreuil battle-field he had to win the day—5,000 francs.

Had the priest been here he would have made a reduction for the old man as well as for the two boys who were longing for the roller skates. He would have felt sufficiently rewarded by their smiles. He would have said, "One way or another this little gift will be returned a hundredfold." But Filot knew that nothing is ever returned a hundredfold, not even double, nor do you ever get back the same that you give.

The success of Emmaus, improvised and based on this faith in man and also on chance (which the priest was wont to call Prov-idence), remained a mystery to Filot. To him living was a matter of life and death, a battle in the night of the jungle. Here in France this battle took on a civilized form, developed with bank-notes, small and large, but the human mass was no less relentless.

Toward evening he sold four trunks to the director of a theater group. They were to be delivered to his house on Rue Changar-nier. Filot brought five 1,000-franc bills and several smaller ones back to Emmaus.

When the street lights went on, Dédé came to pick him up in the truck. Together they loaded up what was left of Filot's merchandise.

Two men were slowly crossing the Boulevard Soult out near Vincennes. One had an accordion slung across his shoulder. He took his friend by the arm.

"You're not going to act up now, are you, Marco?"

"I can feel it coming. Don't leave me alone," moaned the other. "Don't leave me, Henri."

"Good God, can't you control yourself till we get to the woods?"

"Don't let me fall, Henri, don't be a dog."

"O.K. O.K."

His arm started to twitch. No, they couldn't stop at a bistro.
The owner would send for the police. Henri was afraid of cops,
and for a very good reason, too. The best thing would be to
reach the empty lot near the Porte de Vincennes and let Marco
lie down for a while. Maybe it would pass. With a bit of rest
and a glass of hot milk maybe he could get him to the café across
from the subway.

"Wait a minute; let me undo your collar."

His arm was twitching more and more as they crossed the Rue
Changarnier. Then the epileptic's legs gave way. Henri dragged
him onto the pavement and let him down on the ground to have
his fit. He stood aside, wiped his forehead, and lit a cigarette.

"As long as he doesn't start howling."

Luckily at this late hour the passers-by were few and far between. What a thing to happen, what rotten luck—just tonight,
when they were supposed to play at a little bar at the Porte de
Montreuil. That was out now. This was the second fit in a
month. They had exactly 207 francs left, not even enough for
a room.

The fit could last five minutes or it might last an hour. In any
case Marco would be too exhausted afterward to play.

A woman passed by, slowed down, and then quickly crossed
the street, turning around several times.

"She's taken me for a killer; but I can't beat it and leave him
lying there."

Twisting in his fit, the man on the ground began to moan.

"Yes, I'll beat it now, with his accordion. It's worth at least
forty thousand."

He could hear his companion's heels and head beating the
pavement, his nails scraping the asphalt, and this noise froze his
will.

Back of the shuttered windows under which Marco was lying
a radio was blaring music. The sick man howled louder. People
were approaching.

"Shut up. Shut up. For God's sake, keep quiet," pleaded
Henri.

The sweat was sticking to his shirt and his back. He stood
aside. Well, then, let them call the cops, let them take Marco,

throw him back in prison, send him to the infirmary for a couple of weeks. The most he risks is the Nanterre asylum. As for me, why should I play hide and seek with bad luck?

Henri was wanted by the Rouen police. It was a six-months-old count: burglary of houseboats.

"I'm beating it," he repeated, never moving an inch.

Suddenly from behind the shutters the radio was turned off and the concierge, in his shirt sleeves, half opened the door. A shaft of light fell on the sick man. Lying on the ground, he was shaking like a marionette. The concierge threw a terror-filled glance at Henri. He was thinking: "This is a gang war."

"My friend is sick," called Henri hastily, before the man had closed the door. "He gets these fits from time to time."

The door slammed shut, then reopened slowly, stayed ajar. The man advanced his large head, seemed to hesitate, and then said:

"Sick? If he's sick he can't stay there."

"There's nothing to be done. He's best left alone."

"You have a drugstore close by."

Henri answered furiously: "Good God. When I tell you there's nothing to be done . . ."

The concierge looked at him suspiciously.

"I'll put a call through." Then he closed the door.

"Now I'll be off," said Henri once again.

At that precise moment a small truck turned the corner and slowed down. The headlights lit up the sick man on the ground and the youth standing next to him.

"What goes on here?" said Filot placidly, sticking his head out of the window.

"My friend is sick."

"Get him home."

"We haven't a home."

Filot pulled back his head and spoke in a low voice to Dédé. Then: "Can we get him in the way he is?"

"Yes, I think the fit has passed."

Marco, unmoving now, seemed to be asleep. A little saliva was trickling from his mouth. His eyes rolled slowly back to normal and closed. His torn, bloody fingers relaxed.

He awoke in the Emmaus dormitory.

23: *An Evening with Friends*

Y O U'L L never make ends meet," said the old consul slowly,
carefully studying his cigar. He was Madame Gilbert's
father.

The guests fell silent and watched the priest. This was a dinner between intimate friends at the Gilberts'. The Father had
accepted the invitation in order to see his friends: two members
of Parliament, an intellectual Hindu disciple of Gandhi, Monsieur Gilbert the old lawyer, and their hostess.

"You don't know all the Father's resources," said Monsieur
Gilbert. "If he were in business he'd be running us all a merry
chase."

"The Father has plunged headlong into something he'll never
be able to get out of," repeated the old man obstinately.

"If I got into it, why should I try to get out?" queried the
priest.

The consul threw a furious look at him. The others smiled,
all except the Hindu, whose eyes never left the Father's face.

Madame Gilbert offered the priest a dish of fruit.

"Father, you've eaten absolutely nothing. At least have some
fruit."

"Gladly."

The consul went on smoking his cigar, looking extremely annoyed. This story of Emmaus he had just been listening to left
an unpleasant taste in his mouth. He felt uneasy. He would
have preferred not to have known about it at all. The world's
misery, this abyss which makes you giddy when you look into it,

this curse which compromises all peace of mind had no place at all in a social gathering. His cigar tasted bad. The evocation of poverty makes everything taste bad. Even mentioning it is bad taste in itself. And so conversation, light and animated, started around the table.

The priest was pensively peeling an apple.

"Why didn't you eat anything? Are you ill, Father?"

"No, indeed," said the priest. "You must forgive me."

He was thinking: "With all that they served us today, the entire community could have been fed." But how could he hurt his hostess's feelings?

The consul lifted his hand and spoke, stressing each syllable: "Ra-tion-a-lize. That's what one must do. Place the problem of misery on a technical plane!"

"Why not?" said the Father. "Technical charity . . ."

The Hindu frowned.

"Multiply the foundations and homes?" The old lawyer renewed the attack. "But I don't believe much in that, in small private initiative, nor in state control. It's the large enterprises that should take everything in hand."

"I would not like to arrive at a bureaucratic foundation with numbered case histories, with employees whose devotion is achieved by the pay they receive. Nor do I want to serve as publicity for an enterprise."

And the Father went on to relate how a representative of an *apéritif* firm had come to him with the proposal that the tracts of Emmaus be printed at the expense of his firm, on condition that each one would bear the words: "Offered by X." The Father had replied: "At the crossroads of misery where I stand, I know that your product is largely the cause of the misfortune I see."

"But you are terrible!" cried the consul. "To fight poverty you must use efficient means! And what are your means?"

The Father answered with the calm born of evidence:

"Live with them. Give your life."

"Give your life? And you imagine for a moment you can succeed by placing yourself from the start in losing circumstances?"

The priest shrugged.

"Loser . . . winner? What does all that mean? Christ, to your way of thinking, did He win . . . or lose?"

"I respect . . ." grunted the consul.

He did not end his sentence and instead drew a long breath, "Phew." Then, lowering his voice:

"One must not make men conscious of their shame. One must not make their lives impossible."

"Now, Papa, really, don't torment the Father," said Madame Gilbert, rising.

"It's he who is tormenting me," growled the consul, getting up painfully from his chair. He went up to the Father and in a confidential whisper asked:

"At least are they grateful to you?"

"To begin with, is this a rule for one's actions? But yes, yes. Only a few days ago four or five of them came to my office bringing me a little clock into which they had inserted an electric bulb that illuminated an image of the good Samaritan. They make a thousand other kind and wonderful gestures."

"And do you talk to them of God?"

"No. It's they who talk of Him first, the minute they get drunk."

"Hmm," said the consul.

They went to the drawing room. Their hostess turned on the radio. The jovial voice of an auctioneer came to them:

"Thirty-two thousand francs. Do you wish to continue?"

"Yes."

"Sixth question: Who was the first president of the Third Republic?"

The priest murmured: "Thiers: from 1871 to 1873."

"Why don't you get in on this radio quiz?" suggested one of the Parliament members. "It's called 'Double or Nothing.'"

The priest smiled.

"Become a circus clown? Serve as publicity agent for some famous product?"

"Why not? It's a way of getting out of the hole."

"And if I fail? I do not want to bring the cloth into ridicule."

"But after all," cried the consul, "it's money that makes the world go round."

The Hindu, still silent, never took his intense gaze off the priest's face.

"Of course," he murmured.

Madame Gilbert changed the station, and music took the place of the frantic auctioneer's voice. A Brandenburg concerto. The full harmony burst into sound like a flame. The themes, joined to each other with a burning and deliberate passion, recalled the reflection of water in a rapid stream, pure and icy. The friends fell silent. The Father had closed his eyes.

"This, too, this joy, too, is forbidden me. To live with them is to blend myself to other joys in accordance with their standards. Art, poetry, music are lovely things, but only they count. I must not seek escape. Tonight is exactly that."

He started. The consul was shouting into his ear:

"Money. You depend on money . . ."

The priest forced a smile.

"Our subsistence depends on our work," he said. "This insures our independence and permits us to accept gifts and loans from anyone. We give no account of them and we accept even from those whose money comes from a doubtful source."

The consul let his breath out in a low whistle that meant defeat.

The Hindu made a gesture and stopped.

"The more I think of it, the more practicable it seems to me," said the Parliament member. "Present yourself to the 'Double or Nothing' people. The show will be in the Paris area next week. It would be marvelous for Emmaus."

Then the Father looked at his Hindu friend and smiled.

"What do you think of this, Mahani?"

In a muted voice the sage replied:

"Who would not, to save his child, jump into a mire of mud?"

A few days later the Father received a note from the consul.

"You shook us up," he wrote. "One needs it sometimes. Thank you. I am enclosing a check for 5,000 francs."

24: *Djibouti*
Machines and Beasts

IN THE spring Djibouti left the Clos Fleuri construction team
and returned to Emmaus.

The priest had asked him whether he knew how to drive and
whether he had his permit.

"Yes, Father, but I'd rather not drive. It brings me bad luck."

"Are you superstitious?"

Djibouti related to the Father the story of his accident near
Étampes.

"Will you take over the mechanical repair shop then?"

"Yes, that's in my line."

"Now that we have seven cars, it's one of our most important
posts."

Djibouti installed a little workshop between the garage and
the kitchen garden. He kept his tools there and slept there, too.
All day long and often into the night he could be seen bent over
one of the pathetic secondhand jalopies that belonged to the community. He felt sorry for these broken-down cars. He cared for
them with solicitude and competence. And his life continued
on, calm, laborious, and solitary.

But on Sunday Djibouti went over to Clos Fleuri with sweets
or a toy for Noëlle. He ate with the Vatiers and would often
spend his afternoon there. If the weather was good, they would
all go for a walk along the river.

The men at Emmaus called Djibouti "the Bear," said that he

hadn't a friend in the world, that he was a lone wolf who only talked to himself. And it was quite true that when he stuck his head under the hood of a car Djibouti usually talked to himself half aloud. He would address the engine. He would carry on a conversation with the motor as a doctor with his patient, questioning him about what ailed him, scolding him for being so stubborn, and reproaching him for his obstinacy.

Djibouti had no special friend at Emmaus. The friendship of things, of his machines and tools sufficed. And to those wornout motors and cars that were threatened with the junk heap he would devote himself with an almost fraternal solicitude. He had always felt a passionate friendship for the "ancestor," the ancient 1925 Renault bought during the first days of the campaign "*chine.*" It had had at least twenty breakdowns, and the Father had said that it was beyond all hope.

"A vicious old hag," thought Djibouti, every time he saw her hauled home by a truck. "Rotten with caprice. Here we go again," he muttered. "You don't care two hoots about us, eh! You're just being pigheaded. But wait a bit, old girl, till I get my hands on you."

Frowning, his scarred face flushed with anger, he would grab the monkey wrench. But his rage would fade quickly. You can't be mad at a sick animal. She had to be nursed with tenderness and patience. One had to restore her confidence in herself, tame the wayward will.

"Look, you wouldn't want me to chuck you onto the junk heap, would you? Or that I should send you to the smelting pot, would you? What is it this time? Ah, I was afraid of that, that you would go and bust a magneto. But I didn't think it would be so simple. Well, my girl, you're not going to get a new one, it's too expensive. I'll fix this one up for you."

A rich man can despise things, waste them, destroy them, or use them without love. He can even replace a car he has stopped liking. The poor man is tied to his poor belongings. He is forced to love the poor things that are his only worldly goods. And at length the things return this love. As he took it apart, Djibouti could feel the sick old soul of the magneto responding to his anxious care, that poor simple life aspiring to health, to a new use.

"It was as simple as that," he grumbled, in a low voice. "There was a blade loose. There, you screws, don't run away now. Come on now," he said, taking out the armature, "let me at you! Don't be that way. Tsk, tsk . . . Don't worry there, you wires, I'll get to you in a minute."

He slapped his palm against the tin body of the old Renault. "You'll roll again whether you like it or not, old mule, and the Father will be happy."

The others could well say Djibouti was a "talk-to-himself" savage who needed only his own company. But Abbé Pierre understood him. One day he had told him that "inanimate objects receive a kind of incarnation and participate in the world's redemption." Though Djibouti had not the slightest idea of what the priest was talking about he fully approved. These complicated words were way beyond him.

Next to the garage was the wrecking shop. Djibouti could hear the hammering, the squeak of the saw as it attacked the condemned things. These noises hurt him. He would not have wanted to work on wrecking jobs. He admitted their utility, for the iron could be melted and reconverted into metal that would become a bright new car. Maybe that was what the Father meant by the "resurrection of all things."

His devotion to the Father and his affection for the cars, the humdrum life of the community, Noëlle and her parents, this was Djibouti's world—and it was enough to fill his old heart. And then there were the animals at Emmaus, and the dogs. His own mutt, Finaud, had never left his side since the day he had picked him up at La Barrière. He had also done the job with him on the Clos Fleuri lot, and he'd gone secondhand dealing and ragpicking, too. And now he sat and watched while Djibouti worked in the garage.

Finaud's friendship was not a jealous one. On spring evenings, when they were not too hard pressed by work, he would accompany Djibouti to the chicken coops, to the pigsties, and the kennels. Léon, the "menagerie" chief, had enjoyed Djibouti's esteem ever since a certain Sunday afternoon. "The Bear" had drunk a glass of wine at the crossroads café with some of the other Companions of Emmaus, a very unusual thing for him to do. At six o'clock Léon had stood up to go.

"Well, boys, guess I'd better be getting along."

"Keeping your girl friend waiting?"

"No, my animals."

Léon was a calm and jovial athlete. He had been a volunteer in the navy, egged on by his taste for travel. But he soon changed his tune. There wasn't much moving around on a naval vessel. Obstinate, not eager for discipline, he spent twelve months in jail as a matter of "honor." Irregular shore leaves, AWOL, answering back to his superiors, fights, escapes. . . . He loitered in Marseille. His physical strength and good looks insured his success in the red-light district. But Léon left there because of an incomprehensible need for cleanliness. He had been eking out an existence in Paris for three months when word reached him of Emmaus. He asked the priest to allow him to care for the animals. His unstable character had at last found something to cling to, and since he had found that someone was waiting for him he had become a different man.

To care for three pigs, chickens, and ducks, twelve dogs and, very soon, a goat, was no small job. Every day in the back of the park, with the waste furnished by the kitchen, he cooked the pigs' soup in a large bin. He cleaned the sty, fed the bread to the chickens, and went around the three kennels.

Certain of the dogs had been picked up on the street or at the city dump. They were mongrels and most affectionate. Like the men, they had known the despair of solitude on the empty streets, they had known hunger, cold, nights outdoors, and that had not made them cruel. In their errant lives they had accumulated an immense stock of affection which they expressed at last for those who brought them their food and a few kind words. Never were they brutalized by the Companions of Emmaus.

"Animals are very important to Emmaus," the priest would often say.

Important, yes. For these affectionate creatures were not without influence on the men to whom life had so often refused the chance to love and be loved. And the men at Emmaus loved their animals, less through sentiment than through a sense of solidarity. Some had been given to them in the course of the secondhand-dealing expeditions; or a neighbor had asked them to take care of his spaniel while he was away and had never re-

turned. And the cats. They swarmed round the kitchen. People
around the district knew that Emmaus was open to all and would
come and leave their kittens on the lawn at night.

In a hovel in the suburbs the Companions had discovered an
old woman dying of hunger. She had eighteen cats. They had
picked up some of them, and let the others loose. The mad
woman complained to the Society for Prevention of Cruelty to
Animals.

When Emmaus began to get short of bread, the men separated
the dogs. The mongrels made good guardians for the families
living at Clos Fleuri. But the pedigreed dogs were sold to a
Champs-Elysées kennel, not without regret nor a feeling of guilt.
Animals, after all, aren't just so much merchandise. One day
Léon sold a pretty little terrier. The dog found its way back,
jumping, crazy with joy, rolling all over the ground, and so
happy that he couldn't bark. Léon took off his expensive collar.
He threw it into the fire without reading the owner's name.
Abbé Pierre scolded him and next day went back to the shop to
refund the money. But they kept the dog.

On spring evenings they would turn the dogs loose in the
park. Léon and Djibouti would sit and peacefully smoke a cigarette under the blossoming apple tree, watching the joyously
yapping pack romp and play.

And the money Djibouti earned, 400 francs a week, he put
aside in the National Savings Bank in the name of his little
friend Noëlle.

✳ III ✳

HOPE SPRINGS ETERNAL

25: *"Double or Nothing"*

THE FATHER found it difficult to consider seriously the idea of entering the "Double or Nothing" quiz contest. This project was never further from his mind than on the day when he found himself passing through Chantilly driving a truckload of old furniture, product of a day's collecting at Senlis.

"Look, a circus," said the youth who was riding with the priest. The tent was pitched on the esplanade, surrounded by several colorful wagons. A crowd was wandering around the edge of the white fence. The spring sunshine gave the scene a festive air shining on the roofs of the cars, the gaily-painted fronts of the menageries, the multicolored trimmings that were hung out for the parade. The breeze ruffled the banners and publicity bunting. Coming from the huge tent, already filled with the afternoon crowd, came the sounds of music interrupted by the voice of the loud-speaker, applause, and laughter. That day was the opening performance of the season, the first show of the ten-month trek the circus would make across France.

"Is this the 'Double or Nothing' circus?" asked the Father.

He stopped the car by the fence, against which a man wearing a red cap was leaning.

"What are you doing, Father?" asked his companion. "Does all this tempt you?"

"Yes, it does."

He stuck his head out of the car window.

"Say, what do you do about getting into the 'Double or Nothing' quiz?"

The man, taken by surprise, looked first at the priest and then at his truck loaded with old chairs and tattered mattresses.

"Over there is François Chatelard's wagon," said the man, touching his cap. "You'd better see him."

By the end of the afternoon the quiz candidates who had put down their names for the evening show found themselves sitting together on a café terrace. François Chatelard was about to give them an elimination examination. There were ten of them including a young woman who was doubtless a schoolteacher. The men, kidding each other mainly to hide their jitters, were repeating:

"What do we risk? Why not give it a try?"

With curiosity they noted the arrival of a bearded priest who sat down with his companion at the edge of the group.

The setting sun shone on the square, the trees, the crowd of gay stragglers coming out of the circus. The priest was not quite at ease. Had he the right to take part in a publicity stunt for this commercial enterprise even though it was representing merely a cake of soap? He was now "deep in the mire" mentioned by his Hindu friend. He was going to take the risk—and in a few moments maybe he would be beaten at the test. The thought of failure did not trouble him so much. All this seemed only half real. The real problem was Emmaus. . . .

François Chatelard entered. Small, round, alert, carrying a brief case, he sat down at a table and had the entrants called in turn. Only three of them would be retained for the evening's performance. He took from his jammed brief case his file where the questions were classified according to category.

"On what subject do you prefer to be quizzed, Father?"

"It's all the same to me," answered the priest.

"Well, if you like, we'll pick a specialty we don't often have a chance to use: current events."

"Fine for current events."

Chatelard handed him a white sheet of paper and a pencil.

"Here's my first question. You write the answer."

That evening about ten o'clock, while the first part of the show was under way, Zappy Max, the vaudeville star, came to stick his head in the window of Chatelard's wagon. The latter, in his shirt sleeves, was bending over a recording device, working on the "tape" of the afternoon's program. He made the machine talk, shout, sing, and he picked the passages to be broadcast the next day. He would stop it, cut the plastic tape with scissors, paste the ends together, and again release the sound of words and laughter. From the half-hour recording he had made, only a few minutes would actually go on the air; and the cutting he was doing must be imperceptible to the human ear. It was a delicate task of editing which could absorb him for hours, sometimes lasting late into the night. The best parts of the worked-over tape recording would be transmitted by special telephone line to the broadcasting studio in Paris, recorded, and held there until needed. Millions of listeners could thus hear one of their favorite French broadcasts.

"It wasn't too good this afternoon," said Zappy, his head inside the window of the gypsy wagon. "That student told me that *The Journey to the End of the Night* was by Jules Verne."

"We'll do a better job tonight," said François, rolling the recording tape backward and making the machine quack like a flock of angry ducks. "There's a priest there and he's mighty bright."

"What subject did he pick?"

"Current events. The others aren't so hot. Where are we now?"

Zappy listened to the noise coming from the tent. Peals of laughter applauded the running gags of the acrobat clowns.

"The Craddocks," said Zappy. "And there's intermission. I'd better be going. After the show are you going to come eat with us in the castle stables? I'm told it will be really something. Candlelight, hunting horns, men in their hunting pink—all that stuff. . . ."

He imitated the sound of hunting horns.

"I don't know. I've got all this work," said François.

Several young girls' voices outside of the ring were calling: "Monsieur Zappy, Monsieur Zappy!"

"They even know you from your back," said Chatelard.

"I'm so popular," cracked Zappy, rolling his eyes.

He gave a little jump, his head disappeared.

François stopped the machine, cut off the current. Before

boarding the radio truck that would enter the circus ring during the intermission he sat down at his table and picked from his files the questions for the three competitors of the evening. He slipped them into three envelopes.

"Let's see what our bright priest will do," he said to himself. "Let's hope he makes the 32,000."

At the fourth question the priest smiled broadly.

"I see you smiling," cried Zappy. "May I ask why?"

This disconcerted him somewhat, this little priest in his torn windbreaker and muddy shoes who had answered with perfect composure the three political questions that might have thrown specialists. Who was the president of the Counsel in 1947? Which international conferences were held four years after the Armistice? What is the official name of the Indonesian States?

"I am smiling," said the priest, "because I find the fourth question you have asked me curious, to say the least."

"The number of deputies in the National Assembly? But very few French people know it, Monsieur le Curé. If I asked every person in the audience . . ."

"I must tell you—I was a member of Parliament. We were 600."

Zappy started. There was a moment of surprised silence, then the cheers came rolling down from the back rows and soon filled the theater.

"Bravo!" shouted Zappy. "How much, Monsieur Cashier?"

"Sixteen thousand francs. Do you wish to continue?"

"Yes. Why not?"

The uneasiness the priest had felt the moment he mounted the platform and found himself before the mike had vanished. He had accepted the risk of this part he was to play, facing a crowd who were perhaps just waiting for his first mistake. They would have fun watching the man in white, paid to be funny, jump around this priest in his black robe.

But now he felt sure they wanted him to win. They encouraged him with their bravos, this poor priest in his worn windbreaker. They wanted him to win at least a modest sum, which apparently he needed so badly. At least it would pay for a new jacket. After he told them of his rank of ex-deputy, from question to question the feeling of pity changed to one of stupefaction, then to frank admiration. Oh, but this was really becoming quite thrilling! The bid rose higher, and the risk the strange contestant accepted again and again with almost unconscious daring lent an agonizing quality to the game.

In innumerable experiences, congresses and legislative sessions in the National Assembly, election campaigns, committee meetings, the priest had found himself thrown to the public's mercy, armed solely with the resources of the mind. But that was not like this game, this slightly degrading game, financed by a soap manufacturer. He had known how to move, how to upset the opponents' convictions by mere force of a sincere thought. Now he was playing. And after the first four questions it seemed to him that the game was continuing almost without him. He felt as though he had become a spectator himself, watching someone else answering. It was almost as though he were dictating the questions.

"What do the initials F.A.O. stand for?" asked Zappy.

The priest was a friend of the founder of the United Nations' Food and Agriculture Organization. This was what some people call luck.

Seated at a table on the platform behind him a small, bald-headed man was calling the figures, pulling bills out of a cash register. Zappy repeated the figures out loud, just like at an auction sale.

The crowd applauded. Then came the words: "Will you continue?" This was the only sentence that required an effort of him, because it brought up the question of an agreement.

But he plunged deeper and deeper into this "mire to save his child who was in danger." Yes, he would continue. And other figures, so huge that they did not register in his mind, fluttered heavily around him, and the trembling echo was lost in the breathlessness of the audience sitting in the darkened rows.

"Who is the older of the two, Churchill or Stalin?"

"Where did the term bus originate?"

The simplicity of the questions gave him the bizarre impression of trickery; it was as though an adult were questioning a child.

"But Monsieur le Curé," cried Zappy, "you have a phenomenal memory!" And then he stopped his jokes.

The Father measured the excitement of the audience by the intensity of their silence and the sincerity of their cries, "Enough, enough!" He was like the man on the flying trapeze whose daring twists the insides of the audience, but who must not give in to the temptation of going too far lest he lose all. With a little shock, the priest came down to earth. This was no joke. He could now purchase the truck, pay the arrears on Clos Fleuri. This was real, serious. It meant money.

He said: "I'll stop now."

The crowd, relieved, burst into applause. Shaking with excitement, Zappy shouted: "Two hundred and fifty-six thousand francs. You can stop . . . you certainly have a right to. But do you want me to ask you the next question just out of curiosity?"

"If you wish," said the priest.

"Why was the Rue St. Jacques named after the Saint?"

"Because the pilgrims leaving for St. James of Compostella left Paris by that street."

"Bravo. You could have won 512,000 francs!" cried Zappy.

The priest shrugged his shoulders and smiled. The breaks. . . . Monsieur Tiroir, the cashier, came up, his hands filled with large 10,000-franc bills.

Then came the flash bulbs of the news reporters.

"Now in my turn may I ask a question?" said the Father, smiling.

"But of course," said Zappy Max, taken by surprise. "The mike is all yours."

He bowed and with a dancer's light step made way for Abbé Pierre.

The priest advanced. He had at last won the right to play the game the way he understood it. He, too, had a question to put. And not only to the audience in the theater, but to the hundreds of thousands of listeners who tomorrow would hear him across the four corners of France. He had a few words to say, and it was because he needed the opportunity to throw them in the face of the world that he had mounted this platform. Seizing the mike as if it were a sword, he said:

"The question I would like to ask each one of you is the following:

"How much money are you going to send me to build homes for the homeless? For if I have amused you, I am only too happy, but I did not come here for amusement."

And in a few words he explained all about Emmaus.

Two A.M. The priest, surrounded by a dazed crowd, had climbed into his truck and was now on his way home to Emmaus. Behind him the hunting horns blew in the vast Chantilly stables, torches and candlelight reflected on the bright red uniforms of the huntsmen, threw sparkling light on the jewels, the women's dresses, the silver, and the crystal- and flower-decked tables. A young woman passed a silver platter among the guests and the contributions for Emmaus reached half the sum the priest had won at the circus.

On the road, the exhausted Father smiled and reflected on the ways of Providence, so unforeseen and so filled with humor. But after all, what did that heap of bills in his pocket actually represent? Definite salvation for Emmaus? Oh, no, just temporary relief from several worries. For the needs of the community remained tremendous.

Soon the Father was deeply absorbed by the subject. His companion had fallen asleep. Then, suddenly, the motor coughed, sputtered, and died, interrupting his thoughts. Out of gas in the middle of nowhere.

In the distance he saw the scattered lights of La Courneuve. The youth awakened.

"I'll have to walk to the garage; it's two miles from here."

"But, Father, have you enough money to pay for it?"

They had forgotten their winnings. Both burst out laughing. However, since the night was warm, they decided to sleep in the truck.

26: *A Reporter Discovers*
Emmaus

"**S**AY, Chassat," said the editor in chief, "this should make quite a story—the priest who made a fortune on 'Double or Nothing.' Why don't you go over there and write it up? I want human interest, word pictures of tramps gloating over the windfall, anything you can get hold of that's picturesque, pathetic—get it? And get some sob stuff, too. Let me have about fifty lines. Here, I'll give you the address."

Three days later the young reporter was still holding onto the finished article. "This story . . . the chief's got to take it the way I'm writing it. . . . If he cuts or rewrites one line, I'd just as soon it never got published."

And still he hesitated to turn it in. Not that he was short of copy. But his doubts arose from the fact that his story was not at all along the lines of the one his editor had asked him to throw together in fifty lines. For Chassat had discovered Emmaus. The suffering but hopeful soul of the community demanded not only a serious and complete article from him, but more: his own participation in the same struggle.

The reporter was trying to put some order into the batch of notes and impressions accumulated during the morning when, armed with camera and notebook, he had started out before daybreak on his assignment to Emmaus.

On the bus he had said to himself: "Get yourself into a new

frame of mind, Chassat. Be alert, inquisitive, unprejudiced. It's simple: first pretend you don't know a thing about this priest, except that he won 250,000 francs at 'Double or Nothing' and he's head of a charity home. That's all. Boy, what a bore! I'd sure prefer some other kind of interview, a lush actress, maybe. Here's where I get off. There's the street. Why the devil should a tramp's home, a 'court of miracles,' bury itself in this semi-bourgeois neighborhood?"

Climbing the hill, he glanced at the tiny green gardens. Many of them surrounded false well-houses of painted and varnished bricks and had grottoes of ornate rockwork with porcelain cats and doves perched in the trees. They were all done in the naïve rococo tradition of small proprietors who embellish with loving care the shelter of their old age.

The sound of a bell, coming from the top of the avenue, led the visitor on past a new kindergarten school. Couldn't miss it. There was the sign: "Emmaus—Home for Social Action and Center of International Activity."

Strange name for a court of miracles. The wooden gate was wide open, the deep ruts of the entrance way inviting free passage to cars. The house did not give the impression of a refuge. The building was handsome with its porch and balcony. Five large windows faced on the front and the tiled roof was gabled. In the front was a court with bungalows to the side and in the back a park. It might have been the home of a doctor with a regular and rich clientele or of a retired notary with a comfortable income.

" 'The Castle of the Have-Nots.' What a title for the story," thought Chassat.

There was light in the house, in the bungalows, in the tents. The smell of coffee wafted from the little house to the left as the door opened to let in shadows shaking with cold. Half awake, or so they seemed, the men entered the building, one wearing a military cap.

The reporter sniffed the air and let himself be penetrated by the atmosphere where lived the man he had come to interview. This atmosphere seemed more like that of soldiers' barracks or a workers' community than a charity foundation. The hum of a car came from the back of the building. A voice shouted:

"Jean, the monkey wrench?"

"I lent it to Guy."

"Get it back and make it snappy."

The use of the first name, for example, was not in the tradition of a French charity home, nor a barracks, nor a factory. Community life, brotherhood, everyone working together? This did not seem sufficient to explain the bustling, busy atmosphere.

Close to him a man, his arms filled with children's toys, came out of a cellar. He placed the toys carefully in the back of a truck. Gently he asked the reporter:

"Are you looking for the Father, sir? He just finished saying Mass. Watch for him near the porch or over by the refectory."

It was daybreak now. About ten men (no, they certainly weren't tramps, these fellows) were pushing a truck out of the yard onto the street. The wheels just cleared the statues, picture frames, and chairs lined up outside the house.

What an assortment of things! With delight Chassat looked them over. Here was color. From a discarded trinket to the wardrobe with its looking glass, from the stuffed parrot to the rubber boat, from the rags, paper, and scraps of iron to automobiles ready for the junk heap; here were treasures in quantity, objects that surpassed any movie-studio props. This bric-a-brac, devoid of style, reminiscent of every era, invaded the paths, sheds, tents. It filtered into the building and ran over into the vegetable garden like a huge surrealist still life. The truck, loaded to capacity, was starting off. A team was unloading another car.

"Like moving out of a house," the visitor thought as he took in the strangely picturesque scene. A rapid outpour on one hand and a just as rapid moving in on the other. Some things were leaving, others arriving. And regardless of the impression of disorder and confusion that a first glance might give, everything seemed to get done by some preconceived plan. Every man must be specialized, and every object no doubt had its destiny.

The reporter jotted down on his pad: "Ragpickers' enterprise. A small plant and not a charity foundation. Very special atmosphere. Harmony in action. A community at work." He asked one of the workers:

"Can I see the Father?"

"Go and see if he's in the office," said the man, pointing to the porch.

A front office came first, with a telephone, filing shelves, and a typewriter. On the wall were posted a list of names, distribution of the teams, charts of the rolling stock—the working plans of a properly organized business.

"Where is this 'Court of Miracles' the boss imagined?"

Chassat introduced himself to the small man of about fifty who was sweeping.

The man smiled. "Journalist? Just a moment."

He pushed a door in the pine-wood partition. From behind this partition came the sound of several voices.

"You can group your rounds," said the deepest voice with a slight trace of a Swiss accent. "You have three houses in the seventh precinct. Try and get back by noon."

A young voice came back: "The bumper on the Berliet needs soldering and Patoche is sick."

"I'll go and see him. As for the truck, ask Djibouti."

The receptionist announced the journalist. A voice growled: "He's taken the wrong subway, your reporter. This isn't a zoo."

From the other side of the partition Chassat heard this and smiled. Amusing to make a note of that.

The man returned. "The Father's in. He'll be here in a moment. If you wish, in the meantime, you may speak to Monsieur Luc."

"Monsieur Luc" seated him in an armchair and begged to be excused for a moment. First he had to attend to a few things— he had to give a list of addresses to the men who were leaving to collect *la chine*.

"*La chine?*"

They explained to him the meaning of this: collecting unwanted things from people's houses.

"Better note this, too," thought Chassat.

One of the men standing in the office picked up the list, folded it, and left.

Through the transparent fabric that had replaced the window-pane they saw the truck go by with several men standing in the back.

"Off to ragpicking on the dump," said Monsieur Luc for the benefit of the reporter.

"Ragpicking on the dump?"

"Salvage from the city dump."

"Fine. I'll note that, too."

The telephone rang and Monsieur Luc answered it.

"Yes, of course. Trouble is we don't accept women. It doesn't work. . . . Have they been to the Red Cross? . . . We can feed them here but we can't lodge them. I'll speak to the Father. Tell them to come anyhow. They can speak to him themselves. That might be better. . . ."

He hung up with a sigh and then handed a sheet of paper to the second man. He was very thin and wore overalls.

"Here, Raoul. Father left this for you."

The other slowly deciphered the nervous handwriting.

"See about stove under the shed for the Miettes," he read aloud. "Who in the world are the Miettes?"

"That's the family whose place near Rosny burned down last week. The Father moved them temporarily to Clos Fleuri."

"O.K., we'll stop by." He went out.

"Finally," said Monsieur Luc. "Peace at last."

He turned his bald head to the visitor. From behind thick glasses shone a pair of blue eyes. His generous lips had a skeptical expression about them, tinged with bitterness. Later Chassat learned that, after forty years of office routine, Monsieur Luc, incapable of facing the inaction of retirement, had offered his services to Emmaus.

"So you're waiting to see the Father. I'd rather not disturb him now. He's reading his mail. But can I possibly help you?"

"Fine. Can you explain all this to me?" he asked with a sweep of his hand.

The notary had started to "explain" Emmaus when there was a knock at the door. A young man with a bandaged hand came in for treatment. In this profession wounds infect quickly. The notary, doing the best he could, carefully washed the painful wounds.

"I've told you time and again. Why don't you wear gloves?"

"I was, Monsieur Luc—mittens—they were heavy wool socks."

"If there's no improvement by tomorrow you'll have to go to see a doctor in town."

On the floor above the clacking of a typewriter was heard. Mademoiselle was answering the mail. Again there was a knock. The chief cook's head appeared.

"M'sieur Luc, it's the wine bill. The salesman has made a reduction of five francs on the bottle."

"Go and talk to the Father."

The notary resumed his narrative, and Chassat took more notes. The history of an enterprise with no preconceived plan, the successive stages of the home, the hard times, the courage of the Father sustained by his Faith.

"But you, sir, you yourself?" questioned the journalist.

The notary shrugged his shoulders in answer.

"Does he believe? Is he an atheist, a skeptic? In any case, he's a man generous of heart," thought Chassat.

Suddenly the door half opened and a voice said hastily:

"I'm off to the Prefecture. It's about the lot at Hetraie. . . . Can't put it off any longer. I'll be back before noon."

"Father, a moment . . ."

But the door had already closed. The reporter had glimpsed an esthetic face, a long, straight nose, a black beard, dark, feverish eyes.

And soon they heard the sound of a car starting.

"And there you are. It's always this way. I always see him in a rush."

Soon again they were interrupted by the arrival of two architects who were to study the development of a new lot with the priest.

"Paid for by 'Double or Nothing'?" ventured the reporter.

The notary replied that the winnings had made it possible for them to pay a first installment on a new building lot, and they'd been able to buy two secondhand cars. But it took so much money to help, lodge, and give minimum necessities to these empty-handed people who arrived every day. The "Double or Nothing" stake was just a drop in the bucket. He repeated in a low voice:

"Just a drop in the bucket."

The morning wore on. While waiting for the priest's return the reporter went out for a short walk in the park. The pale sun shone through the young green leaves of the chestnut trees. The air smelled of fresh earth and new grass. Chassat explored every corner of the center, chatted with the wreckers, electricians, mechanics, repairmen, shoemakers, and labor hands. He visited the chapel and the refectory, accepted a cup of coffee from a little bearded cook. He watched the carpenters putting up a shed, petted the friendly dogs through the kennel fence. He saw a truckload of junk arrive, its cargo swaying from side to side. It was rapidly unloaded and sorted. He watched cars arrive and leave. A Ford Vedette drew up before the porch and a gentleman armed with a brief case demanded to see "Monsieur l'Abbé." Then a woman pushing a perambulator and a man leading a little girl by the hand timidly entered the gateway and asked to see "the Father."

"See the Father," mused Chassat. "Speak to the Father. It's the Father who will decide. . . . The Father will arrange it all. . . . This is the chorus of the house, the cry of all these lost children."

Noon came, and in the face of all he'd seen he did not have the courage to accept Monsieur Luc's invitation to share the community meal. He went to a bistro at the crossroads and had lunch there. And while lunching he decided that the whole approach of his story would have to be modified. He could not write of the Father and of Emmaus without taking his readers through the muddy fields and construction lots. This adventure at Emmaus had a backdrop which was so complicated and interwoven, so rich in human interest and spirituality that the young reporter suddenly felt lost and discouraged. He was convinced that it would be hard to sell the story, properly written, to his illustrated weekly, stuffed with pictures of pretty girls, of gory current events, backstage gossip, movie news, comic strips, and sports columns. They would only want to publish something shocking or amusing about Emmaus.

No, this angle no longer had anything in common with his impression of the poor priest, star performer of "Double or Nothing." This bit of luck was an insignificant episode when you considered the entire extraordinary adventure that was Emmaus.

"The story will go as I write it—or it won't get in at all," he kept repeating to himself.

Finally he got to talk to the busy priest as he was leaving the refectory that afternoon. His manner was direct, simple, and sympathetic.

"I must go off in the car again," said the priest. "Maybe you'd like to come along with me, that way we can talk. We'll be back around six."

But Chassat did not get a chance to interview him about the "Double or Nothing" quiz.

One of the Companions of Emmaus was installed on the front seat.

"Forgive me," said the priest, starting the car. "The only time I have to discuss questions concerning the home is when I'm driving somewhere. Are you quite comfortable?"

"Perfectly comfortable."

Heavens, how he raced on these suburban roads! The old jalopy creaked and moaned. Her whole carcass vibrated, rang, and squeaked. The Father tore along with the calm of a sleep-walker while talking of Emmaus to his young companion. In the back were stacked a tent, blankets, a mattress, and a small stove. Squeezed in the space that was left and clutching the insecure door, Chassat strained to catch the conversation of the two men. All this was real adventure with all the opportunities for a good story. But for the first time in his journalistic career Chassat had the disagreeable and humiliating impression of being perfectly useless, of being tolerated through kindness. From the moment of his arrival at Emmaus he had been experiencing a sort of inferiority complex, like that of a child among grownups. When interviewing a star, an actress, or a beauty queen, the welcome he was given made him very conscious of the power of the press, of his ability to influence public opinion, and he was proud of his profession, the best in the world. But here, facing these men engaged in a struggle to survive, his role as a mere witness seemed futile. And if his pen only expressed something that would amuse the public, then his visit here would be utterly devoid of sense. In fact, it would become an abuse of confidence. Chassat clenched his fists and vowed once again:

"The story I write will go in the way I write it or not at all."

They left the city limits. There was sunshine on the flowering fields. They were driving to the reeking dump where twenty ragpickers were working in a swarm of flies. Next they would go to the wasteland overgrown with locust and elm trees on the border of the Brie country. This would be Hetraie where the priest was planning to build about thirty small cottages. When they arrived they found a brush-covered field and a family with three children waiting for the priest at the edge of the road. They were waiting for the tent the Father was bringing them. They were the first settlers. Yesterday wandering, today almost settled.

Next stop was at the small local railroad station. Here the Father went into a huddle about purchasing an unused boxcar— one of the forty-men-eight-horses type.

Next came a visit to another field of decaying garbage. Here two gypsy wagons were stationed. The priest entered one of them to comfort a sick woman. From where the Father had parked, Chassat could hear her moaning. Two little girls were playing near the wagon. Finally the Father came out to the car, and just as they were leaving one of the ragpickers came up to bring them a little dog. He was one of eight who belonged to the other wagon. The puppy would join the other dogs at the Emmaus kennels. The Father asked Chassat to take the filthy animal with him in the back seat.

The afternoon was coming to an end. Returning to the suburbs, they stopped to see a junk dealer who purchased scrap iron, then to see a building contractor.

Finally night fell and they passed by the building lot at Clos Fleuri. At the far end of the lot, separated from the "city" by a fence, several sheds had been erected. This was to be the junk depot where the bulk of their merchandise would be stocked, sorted, and sent out. In this way the community would become its own wholesale and retail agent and could do without middlemen.

As he stopped the car in front of the depot, the Father said to Chassat:

"Look over there. That man is an ex-colleague of yours. He's a journalist who has come to work with us. He's been here two months."

Chassat had no desire to interview his fellow reporter. He had enough impressions of his own.

Then the priest and his companion left the car. Chassat, with the dog asleep on his knees, gave way to bitter dreaming.

In the distance he could see two storage tanks looming huge and black against the reddish screen made by the sunset. Lights were burning in the little houses. He could hear strains of music and the barking of a dog. Chassat was thinking of his fellow journalist with mixed feelings of pity and envy for having renounced the most wonderful profession in the world, that of a reporter.

Chassat had not wanted to speak to him. He was afraid of hearing him say:

"Journalism—one day I got fed up with it. I had to do something else, find something real."

Chassat imagined hearing these words. He even imagined the man adding:

"Something constructive."

He, Chassat, would remain true to his profession. Only he would write *all* he believed in, *all* he felt, and always portray the truth, even if it shocked, upset, or hurt.

"The story I write on Emmaus will be printed as it's written."

And the story appeared *as was*.

During the months that followed countless French and foreign papers, regardless of their political convictions, sent their reporters to Emmaus. Television and radio spread the story of Emmaus throughout the world.

A popular and widely read women's magazine, along with others, engaged in a fertile campaign for gifts which came with touching letters.

One of these, from Belgium, was addressed simply to:

"Monsieur l'Abbé. Emmaus. France."

"I am sending you 1,000 francs, and my neighbor, a very poor old lady, also wants to do the most she can. So she is sending you 1,020 francs."

"Here is 100,000 francs. Do not thank me. But do not forget my address so that from time to time you can come and shake me out of my egotism."

In many letters appeared the words, "Thank you for existing."

But to those who expressed merely their platonic enthusiasm the priest felt inclined to say: "You tell me of your emotion and your admiration. Alas, I have not yet been able to cook emotion and admiration in our kitchen."

The fame of Emmaus brought the scandal of the homeless in France and the solution achieved by the community into broad daylight. The priest started on a round of lectures which shook up public indifference considerably.

But the deep meaning of the Home was not modified. For simultaneously with the new aid the flow of distressed cases increased and the problems multiplied. The tree planted in the soil of misery was growing branches which were becoming even stronger, for they were nourished by an inexhaustible fertility.

Then Chassat's story was read by "Casino."

27: *"Casino"*

MARCELLE, the little hotel maid, slipped, smiling, into the room with the closed shutters. Charles D., known as "Casino," was stretched out on the bed in his shirt sleeves. He opened one eye. Beads of perspiration gleamed on his brow. Stormy heat oppressed the town.

"Getting bored, honey?" she murmured.

"Yeah," he answered.

"Here's something to read. I swiped it at the café."

She produced from under her apron an illustrated magazine published three months earlier.

"Thanks," he snapped, making no effort to take it.

She put the magazine on the bed and sat down beside him. Eyes full of admiration, she watched the heavy features framed in a stubby horseshoe-shaped beard.

"Don't you look tall, lying there like that," she said. "And how strong you are, too. Not like other artists."

Then her smile vanished.

"Listen," she said. "I overheard the boss talking about you. It's three weeks that your room hasn't been paid for."

He frowned and after a short silence said:

"Has he got a piano up in his apartment?"

"Sure. His little girl used to play on it before they packed her off to convent school. Why, have you got some idea about the piano?"

"Just thought I might have it brought down to the bar and

play there. It would give the place some atmosphere. See what
I mean?"

"Swell," she said. "And maybe for Saturday dances. He'll be
having a drink now, and that always puts him in a good mood.
Get dressed. I'll go down and about nine I'll bring you something to eat."

A half-hour later Casino went down to the pub. In his hand
he held the small music folder which he had carried with him
for the last twenty years, ever since he started writing songs.

The boss greeted his offer with no enthusiasm at all. "Artists"
somehow rubbed him the wrong way.

"We already have a radio in the dining room."

"Canned music," answered the musician. "You understand
that's not the same as if you had a pianist playing right in the
room."

"Well, for one thing, the piano belongs to my daughter. And,
besides, I'm afraid it'll give the place a bad atmosphere."

"You're wrong," replied Casino, visibly annoyed. "The best
places on the boulevards have their own music. That draws cus-
tomers."

This last argument made the boss hesitate.

"Before we start anything I'd like to know what you can
really do."

"Look at this," Casino said in his deep voice.

And he presented the music folder he had decorated himself
with a painting representing the shores of a lake by night.
Rushes, a small house, a boat, poplars, all were reflected in the
lake in a sugary, romantic style. The shapes and lines seemed
to dissolve in a mist. Casino had produced this masterpiece one
Sunday out of sheer boredom, and it reflected his own character.
In the sky of his painting floated the shape of a woman. She was
curvaceous, lascivious, rather disheveled, and completely nude.
His music probably resembled his painting. In beautiful round
letters the text read:

"Famous hits by Paul D., composer-musician of the Casino,
including: 'Blue Thrills,' 'Tell Me, My Little Wild One,' 'On
the Curtains,' 'Lonely Heart.' "

"My songs were first sung by Dalis, in 1928–29, remember?
We toured the country."

"I don't remember," said the boss.

His wife came and looked over his shoulder.

"This should be pretty!" she exclaimed.

"Well," said Casino, moved suddenly to gallantry. "Madame, I'll play just for you. Choose the song you prefer."

Women annoyed him, but he was not completely devoid of interest in them, for he often thought, "That's how I got here."

She hesitated, then went through the music.

They went into the couple's private apartment, on into a well-polished salon. Casino sat down at the piano, bowed to the hostess, and announced "Blue Thrills."

He hadn't touched a piano since the war. His left hand was stiff, it was awkward for him to keep the beat. He interrupted his playing with exclamations of: "Watch out! It's still a bit rusty right there . . . it's been ten years, you know. . . ." He kept starting over again, trying to get back in tune, the veins on his brow standing out with the effort. In his hoarse voice he struggled to sing the half-forgotten, almost unintelligible words, deciphering them from the sheets of music as he went along.

> "The evenings of madness and passion.
> The thrill of silence . . ."

The boss burst out laughing.

"Haven't you anything a little more up to date, and funnier?"

"Funnier?" Casino, offended, rose and closed the music.

The wife threw him a compassionate glance. They returned to the café.

The host stood them a round of drinks, and when the two men were alone said:

"That's all right. But I must have your room."

"So for the musical performance you might get a small band together?"

"We'll see about that later. In the meantime, you owe me two weeks' rent."

"I'll pay you tomorrow."

"Can I count on that?"

Casino left as if he were going out to dine at a restaurant, but he hadn't the money to pay for a meal. Anyway, he could count on the little maid's promise. She would bring a plate up to his room on the sly.

The air was lighter. It must have rained in the suburbs.

"Dirty dog," growled Casino. "Jealous of me because of Marcelle. If I could, I'd leave tonight. But where can I sleep? Where can I find a quiet place? I'd better try to find some work first."

He bought an evening paper and looked at the "Help Wanted" ads. That was the way to look for work. He turned his steps to the Faubourg du Temple.

"Get out. Or find a way. Escape. Get out, and head south. Maybe with Marcelle. She seems like a girl with guts."

Children were playing and shouting along the quai of St. Martin's Canal. At the bottom of the steps near the dam a tramp was washing his feet. The fringed foliage of the plane trees spread over the edge of the water, bathed in golden light of the setting sun. Here in this corner, out of the way of the infernal carnival of the boulevards, there was silence, the smell of leaves, the fresh smell of green after rain, the smell of a summer evening, so melancholy and anguishing to a tormented soul.

Sitting on a bench in the square facing the canal, Casino felt this dangerous feeling surging in him—first sign of an attack of blues. He thought: "There's only one way to stop this quickly —a good binge." If he allowed the soft, warm evening to get the better of him, if he gave way to the trap of "remembering" here in this corner of Paris where he, too, had played and shouted as a kid, then he would see clearly, and sitting in judgment on himself would be terrible.

But he didn't even have enough money to get drunk. He thought to himself: "Art today doesn't pay, the public never recognizes talent. You have to be launched, you have to have money to do your own publicity." Behind these old excuses he hid the real reason for his failure; which was that he had never had any real talent. The Conservatory had "corrupted" him, he liked to say, made him believe in music. Next the music hall, the small-time orchestra life at the Casino. He was overly fond of women and they returned his feelings, for Casino was a big, strong man, handsome in his way. Women . . . He could become so obsessed that he was almost crazy. That was what had really spoiled it all. And then wine. He had believed in the traditional and idiotic conception of an artist's life. A mediocre player, he had started composing. He had always nursed the thought that one day he would write an operetta. But after four songs he had given that up without, however, renouncing his vocation as a pianist. Women had so often told him he was a genius. On short tours in the provinces he played the piano as often well as badly. Then came the war. Afterward he felt out of touch and hated music. Today, seated at the proprietor's piano, he had realized definitely his failure.

He spat in the canal to rid himself of his disappointment, then lit a cigarette and ran his finger down the want-ad column. Nothing for him. He walked back toward the Place de la République and plunged again into the pitiless purgatory of the big city.

Night had fallen when Marcelle placed the plate and a quarter of a bottle of wine on the table in his room.

"I don't know what he has against you, but he's been saying he's going to call the police unless you pay up before noon tomorrow."

Casino said not a word. He looked at her with hostile eyes, heavy with reproach and silent demand. She understood and flushed.

"I'll see what I can do again," she said. "It's only because it's for you."

Having eaten, he went to bed and leafed through the illustrated magazine the young girl had left. Full of pictures and no text. No need to rack your brains. There were two solid pages filled with comic strips which left him cold. He gave them hardly a glance. What he wanted were pictures of pretty girls and the magazine was filled with them. On page 3: "Miss Molasses," a pretty American pinup wearing a bathing suit that was being tarred and feathered by dignified city fathers. On page 4 a French cancan dancing troupe, kicking high to amuse a colored boxer who had become a music-hall star. On page 8: the "Atomic Countess," a titled girl who had become a gang chief. And mannequins presenting summer styles, film stars, Miss This-and-That, bathing beauties in their skin-tight suits.

Suddenly the picture of a priest. A priest in a black cape. Between a giraffe which had just had a baby in the zoo and a new super-atomic plane story appeared the bearded, thin face of a priest, haunting and out of place. Wearing his cape and carrying a heavy cane, he was standing on a heap of garbage. His expression was suffering yet roguish, and he looked you straight in the eyes. The caption read: "Emmaus, Haven of Lost Souls."

Casino's eyes dropped to the bottom of the page, to a suggestive ad for new bras, then they flashed back to the caption: "Haven of Lost Souls."

"As a last resort," he said to himself.

Three days later Casino crossed the threshold of Emmaus.

28: *Thefts*

Not bad, Mastic, not bad, but if I were you . . ."

"Always brighter than the others, aren't you, Casino?"

Brighter than the others. He didn't give a damn for the others. He despised their good will, their devotion, their naïve idealism, their absurd confidence in the community's future. He had no confidence in the whole Emmaus setup. It might last awhile but not for long. Stick it out and make the most of it until then, though. Men can't be saved when they don't want to be, Casino figured; and most men's souls were mean, lazy, and cynically indifferent. The priest would be crushed by the task of trying to do anything with him. In fact, it was a miracle that he had stood it this long.

Mastic, about forty, was tall, thin, bald, and dressed today in white overalls smeared in multicolored spots. He was a personality at Emmaus, the community's specialized painter. Always busy, jovial, and service-minded, he enjoyed the respect of everyone and could well be proud of his work, whether it was on an old car Djibouti had asked him to do up or an old toy Filot had asked him to restore.

But the work of art closest to his heart was the large shield which he was now hanging over the entrance to Hetraie. Measuring five feet by three and a half, he had painted on its surface the plan of the future "City." There were thirty little white-roofed houses, seen from above, with green gardens and yellow roads separating them. The priest was delighted by this actual

illustration of his dream. When news reporters began to visit the
Hetraie building lot, they would refer in their stories to this
plan, which so movingly prophesied future developments.

"What a beautiful day it will be when those thirty bungalows
become a wood-and-stone reality."

And it would come to pass. Before the end of the year it
would happen. Mastic believed it, and everyone else in Emmaus
believed it, everyone except Casino.

Since his arrival in September he had done different jobs
around the house but could not adapt himself to any single one,
because he, Casino, was *too sly*. His last job had been as office
boy, and now he slept in the same room as Mastic, near the
carpenter's shop. He had kept in touch with Marcelle and met
her every Saturday night. She wanted him to leave his tramps
to find a job in Paris so they could live together. But Casino
calmed her impatience. He was waiting for the right moment to
leave.

With the October rains there was a new stream of volunteers,
many of whom were old men seeking a refuge rather than a place
to work. That the press had publicized Emmaus so widely was
in some ways a disservice. The priest repeated time and again
that Emmaus was "not a home, but a workers' community."
However, when they insisted, he let them stay. In this way old
man Tienne took his place in the community.

He had installed himself in the room with Casino and Mastic.
Every other corner was taken. Tienne and Mastic had met before at Nanterre. From time to time, on evenings when rain
hammered on the roof above their room, they would open a bottle and reminisce about their stay at the Home, that immense
caravansary of unfortunates, human failures, good-for-nothings,
half-wits, and social outcasts.

Casino listened to them, smoking his pipe and grimacing,
telling them that all that mattered in life was dignity. Tienne
and Mastic would nod. "Dignity, that's it."

"You eat, you sleep at Nanterre. They don't ask you where
you're from or where you're going. They just let you sit and
stagnate."

However, old Tienne retained a kind of nostalgia, which the

wine awakened, of his months in that strange city of 5,000 souls, each one picturesque, pitiful, or curious. They were crooners, beggars, turn-of-the-century dandies, African war veterans, repatriated convicts from Cayenne, Foreign Legion veterans, lost children, fallen adventurers, or destitute victims of the Paris jungle—outcasts from everywhere, men and women with no futures.

While drinking a second bottle, both men waxed sentimental over the memory of Josephine, the bisexual singer; over "Maurice, the Grenade," whose fame dated from the time he threw a hand grenade out of his window onto a chattering group of Arabs who were keeping him awake; over Guyot, the jockey—disqualified for having beaten his horse; over Oudinot, the assassin-tramp of the Bois de Boulogne; and other equally dubious celebrities who were sheltered in this sad place.

"No, I won't go back there," said Mastic. "And I'll tell you why. Because of the Father and my friends here. Also because I work, and *what I do will stay done*."

Old Tienne stopped to think about that. In Nanterre, his worst enemy had been idleness. What one misses most in life is work, the kind one likes to do. Shelling beans wasn't exactly his type of job, but he didn't really know what was. Here he tinkered at carpentering. That kept him busy without tiring him too much.

"As for me," thought Casino, "I am an artist, too, but I haven't found my place in the sun." He felt a dull grudge toward life in general welling up within him.

When Casino arrived at Emmaus, the Father had asked him to organize some of the men into a small choir, but he immediately objected. He said that in a group with such little talent, incapable of singing a true note, the result would be pitiful.

"What does the result matter? We haven't enough singing at Emmaus, and the chapel walls will be indulgent."

The truth was that Casino refused to let himself become a part of the community or to share with the others the gift of music that had been bestowed on him. In this way he betrayed his artist's soul, and therein lay the secret of his damnation.

Old Tienne was a capitalist. That is to say, he had a postman's pension—he proved it by showing his well-filled wallet to his two pals. These 25,000 francs monthly would have permitted him to live in the city in mediocre fashion but in liberty. But he was afraid of solitude. With no family, nothing to occupy him, and no one to talk to, he became neurasthenic. He had to have friends, to be able to talk to people he knew in a homelike atmosphere.

"That's why I went to Nanterre. And that's why I'm here with the Father."

"He's terrific," said Mastic. "I'd do anything for him."

"Same here," said Étienne. "Your health, Casino. What's the matter? Can't you say anything!"

"Here's to you."

"But how did you, a specialist," asked Tienne of Mastic, "how did you land in Nanterre?"

"That seemed to be the only place to go when I got out of prison."

From 1946 to 1949 he had worked for a decorating contractor spraying paint by the square mile on movie props.

"I didn't even know what they were supposed to represent; they were too big. But I like to do stuff like that, you know, except now I've lost the feel, and besides it doesn't pay enough."

So to pad his pay he had stolen several buckets of paint which he resold to friends. He spent six months in prison.

"Yes, six months, and I'm not ashamed of it—when I think how they played me for a fool. A man wouldn't become a thief if he wasn't robbed himself, if there was a fair deal between him and his boss."

The first robberies at Emmaus occurred during the priest's absence. He had gone to the east of France on a lecture tour. Monsieur Luc first noticed that five blankets which had been stocked in a corner of the office were missing.

"They were cold," said the Father on his return, "and they helped themselves, but they certainly might have told us."

The incident closed there.

And when Filot saw that there were two pairs of rubber boots missing from a box received the night before, the Father said once again that the comrades who had taken them were in the wrong but that they had probably taken them because of the bad weather. André, the engineer, now head of the ragpicking teams, offered to make a general search.

"No need to make a scene because of these boots," said the Father.

But when several days later young Danou timidly came to report that someone had lifted a new soldering iron right out of his workshop the evening before, the Father listened attentively, though he said to the boy that no doubt the comrade would return it. However, he decided to take up the matter and speak to everyone about it the following Sunday.

"Sometimes one must be fooled, but the interests of the community must not suffer."

Every Sunday after Mass a community meeting was held in the refectory. From distant places where they camped in tents or gypsy wagons, from the building lots of La Hetraie and Clos Fleuri, from the depot at La Réserve, the Father's fold arrived on cycles or in trucks.

They found at the Home the permanent Emmaus Companions—the ragpickers, the wrecking squads, the reparation and maintenance teams. Every Sunday morning they gathered with the Father, who gave them his instructions and briefed them on the progress of the enterprise. In this way each person was conscious of the community's unity, of its aims, of the spirit which cemented it. The dispersed community regrouped itself around the Father, to renew its family spirit, and on these Sundays Abbé Pierre also initiated the newcomers in their rights and duties.

What a revelation this initiation was to some of them. Here they were told that they were no longer charity wards or low-salaried laborers, but free workers. They were made to understand that the enterprise depended on their voluntary adherence, on their competence and courage. Moreover, by their own work they would help those who were poorer than they, help shelter families, save children, and permit penniless young couples to cling to life.

The men arrived at the Home from every horizon of misfortune. After their first night there they listened to this new voice, saw with their own tired and fear-filled eyes this man who had taken their bodies and souls in charge, giving them the key to salvation and dignity. He never raised his voice to them. Seated at a table in the refectory with them, he related, often jokingly, the multiple problems of the community. He talked as man to man, asking their advice and treating them as friends.

This Sunday the Father read aloud to them letters from former Companions, who, after having lived at Emmaus, had taken to the road again and found work. One of them enclosed 1,000 francs. Another asked if he might return to Emmaus because, he wrote, "In the shop where I work as a salesman I do not know for whom or for what I am working."

Then he opened his account book and told them about the financial situation. There was a deficit and he stressed the necessity of working to eliminate it. The winter relief work had strained their resources and expenses had increased considerably. They had also purchased a gypsy wagon from the circus "where I clowned." Then he requested better discipline in the house. Lights should be turned off by 10 P.M., the sleeping quarters should be kept cleaner, and k.p. should be rotated—he hoped everyone would take his turn willingly so that visitors would have a good impression of the house. And there was some rowdiness in the tents out at Clos Fleuri at night that kept the families who lived nearby awake.

"We have installed those families to improve their existence. You must respect the women and children and not undermine all that we have accomplished with such great pains. We cannot keep those who disturb the peace. And we will be very severe with those who drink. And the waste . . . You leave the dining hall with five and six pieces of bread as if you were afraid of being deprived of it. You have known hunger. For years on end you have retained a fear of hunger, yet you take more bread than you can eat and throw it away when it gets stale. You must eat all you want *here* and prevent this waste. Are there any complaints that you are rationed?"

"No, no."

They all agreed they had enough food. They remembered how, before coming to Emmaus, they had lived off vegetable peelings and decayed fruit collected in the markets, with, from time to time, a bowl of soup at the Bread Crumb. They remembered the horror of lines of famished beggars at the doors of the poorhouses.

Then the priest's voice grew graver.

"Something more. About gas. It has been brought to my attention that for a half-hour errand a whole tank has been emptied. I won't say which car this was. If the tank is leaking, it must be fixed. But if someone is exchanging the gas for wine, this is a crime."

He lowered his eyes so that he would not see their faces. He stood with his shoulders slumped, as though crushed by their failings, by their betrayal of confidence—confidence that was taken for granted in the community. In a low, dejected voice he said:

"Among us there are thieves. Several thefts have been committed within the past few days. The community has been robbed, and our own comrades are the victims. If this continues we will have to let the police handle it. We never like the police to interfere in something that concerns us. On the other hand, we cannot tolerate a black sheep at Emmaus."

Again he avoided looking at their faces. He asked them to return the stolen objects.

But nothing was returned. And suspicion entered Emmaus. Djibouti had to make keys for the workshops and rooms. And each man going off to work put his few belongings carefully away in his locker. No one left anything personal around that could be taken. In the workshops the tools were listed. When meeting or visiting a comrade each man thought: "Maybe he did it. Why not?"

One evening, when Mastic was gone, Tienne and Casino were discussing the events of the day.

"Can't be otherwise. It's inevitable," said Casino. "With all the jailbirds around . . ."

Two days later a quarrel broke out between Casino and Mastic. Mastic had called him a lazy rotter.

"Well, one thing's for sure—I've never gone to prison for stealing," said Casino.

"You dirty dog!" said the other, white with rage and clenching his fists.

"Here we don't talk about the past," said Tienne. "You leave that behind when you pass the gate on your way in."

Young Henri, the boy who had been caught pillaging the houseboat at Rouen, was losing all the peace of mind he had found at Emmaus in the eight months he and his friend Marco had been there. He kept thinking: "Maybe the Father had me in mind when he mentioned the black sheep. Maybe he knows." He was scared; he could not sleep. He kept seeing the face of the little old lady he had robbed ten days ago.

It had happened this way. Headed by Philippe, the ragpicking team to which Henri and his friend Marco belonged was going that morning to a toyshop that had offered some unsalable toy dogs. In addition to these they found wooden horses, broken dolls, plush Teddy bears eaten by moths, chess games with one piece missing, and small mechanical automobiles with broken springs. All these could be repaired at Emmaus for Christmas distribution to the Clos Fleuri children. While Philippe and the others were transporting the merchandise from the back of the shop to the truck, Henri went to ring doorbells in the neighboring houses.

"Anything for sale?"

Suspicious at first, one of the concierges finally opened his door when Abbé Pierre's name was mentioned. "Ah, yes, of course, the priest of the 'Double or Nothing' quiz." He accepted the tract which Henri handed him and promised to put it up near the mailboxes. He then added: "By the way, the dressmaker on the third floor mentioned a wardrobe she has for sale."

Henri went up to the third floor. A little old lady opened the door and, peering with large frightened eyes from behind steel-framed glasses, said:

"Oh, Monsieur, the dressmaker lives just across the hall over there. I don't think she's home, though. I heard her going downstairs about half an hour ago."

Henri turned to leave.

"But please . . . wait a minute," said the little old lady. "I've heard about Abbé Pierre, too, and I can't let you leave empty-handed. Let me give you something I've been saving for him. Would you please wait a moment?"

The object was not very large, but was heavy for its size. It was a mysterious little cylinder wrapped in paper.

"This is for Monsieur l'Abbé . . . and . . ."

She hesitated, looking intently at him with eyes as blue and innocent as a child's.

"Ask him to remember me in the Prayer for the Living. Tell him, Monsieur, won't you?"

"Prayer for the Living." Henri memorized it while he was going down. "I'll tell the Father, sure, but what does it mean? And that little roll? What could weigh so much that comes wrapped in paper?" In the entrance hall he carefully unwrapped the package. There were ten coins—ten twenty-franc coins, in gold.

So easy, so tempting to keep a treasure passed from hand to hand without any witnesses. And the others knew nothing about it. The old lady would never talk. He weighed the pieces in his hand. How easy it would be to say to the others:

"Say, boys, you go on home without me."

There was nothing to hold him at Emmaus. That evening someone else could have his bed and once again he would roam Paris, free. And before all the money was spent he would have time for a look at the future.

Clutching his loot, Henri walked toward the truck where his comrades were finishing their job.

At that moment his friend Marco stepped out of the shop carrying a wooden horse, a little yellow horse with a proud and independent look in his painted black eyes.

"Gee," thought Henri, "I had a horse like that when I was a kid." At Clos Fleuri a child would get the toy for Christmas. But who the hell cares about the horse or the kids at Clos Fleuri? Now he held a fortune in his fist. Freedom.

He walked up to Philippe, who was stacking the toys in the truck, to tell him he was not going back with them to Emmaus. But he stopped. There was Marco. Marco. He couldn't let *him* down. Marco, his wretched friend who would call him in that pitiful voice as he felt a fit approaching: "Henri, Henri, I feel it coming. Don't let me fall." No, he couldn't let him down.

So they returned to Emmaus together, and Henri gave Philippe the old lady's coins—except for one which he kept for himself.

This tenth coin he returned to the Father on Sunday evening. And the Father, his head in his hands, listened silently to Henri's confession. When Henri had finished, Abbé Pierre, shaking with fever and fits of coughing, looked at him as if he did not know him. Henri was scared. But suddenly a smile appeared on the feverish face and the priest said:

"I thank you, Henri. The Lord has granted us a fine ending to a really sad day."

Then he started to cough again, heartbreakingly.

Ten days passed peacefully without any disturbing new events. At the doctor's repeated insistence the priest went to bed, but from there he continued to watch over his community. On the tenth day old Tienne came to complain that 17,000 francs had disappeared from his wallet. But, as usual, he had noted the numbers of the bills.

With a temperature of 104 degrees, the Father got up to talk to the police. In Marcelle's room at a Paris hotel they were able to recover some of the goods that had been stolen from Emmaus.

Fifteen days after Casino's arrest, Henri met one of his former Rouen associates driving a luxurious sports car in Paris. The man told him that the case of the robbed boathouses had been closed, so why not come and join the rest of the gang in Normandy?

"No, thanks, really," said Henri. *"I can't live that way any more."*

On his return to Emmaus, Henri asked to be allowed to leave the junk-dealing team and work as a ragpicker on the city dumps or on a building lot that was situated still farther out. Marco followed him to La Hetraie, where they joined Denis, the seminarist.

29: *La Hetraie*
Denis's Departure

H ENRI lit the storm lamp.
"I'll bet the truck won't come by for you tonight," he
said to Denis, who was closing his suitcases. "It's snowing too
hard. You'll have to sleep here."

Denis pressed his nose against the tiny window of the railroad car that had been transformed into a dormitory. He watched
pensively as La Hetraie disappeared in the snowstorm and dusk.
Through the whirling blizzard he could vaguely distinguish
ghostlike roofs and trees. The black woods, the large tents that
sheltered the ragpickers' gleanings, the other tents and wagons
were barely visible under the white tide. Not a light flickered.

The "forty-men-eight-horses" car served simultaneously as
cooking, eating, and sleeping quarters. In the back, old man
Tardi cooked their meals on a little stove. At the other end, between the beds and straw mattresses that rested on the floor,
there was another tiny stove for heating. These two small stoves
did not, however, completely solve the problem of keeping the
makeshift shelter warm. Cold winds blew through the old car
and the ceiling lamp flickered in the draft. It made one think of a
ship.

Tardi was in the kitchen. Marco, Henri, the sick student who
was in bed, Kurt the violinist, and Denis were waiting for the

four comrades who had gone two miles away to the neighboring town to buy wine to celebrate Denis's departure. The latter, after an apprenticeship of eight months at Emmaus, was going to enter the seminary and be ordained. His apprenticeship had taught him, as he had hoped it would, the trials of true suffering and life.

Kurt, the Austrian refugee, was sitting on his bed in the corner plucking at the strings of his violin to tune it. Every evening he played for at least a quarter of an hour "to keep from losing his touch." His artist's hand was daily losing its deftness and speed from unloading heavy articles in the icy cold weather. With despair he saw it becoming as rough as the hand of a workman; his fingers were becoming stiff.

But the ex-professor from Vienna did not give in to this progressive deterioration of his fingers, and every evening he brought out his violin, the only possession he had brought with him into exile. He played Brahms, Liszt, and Mozart, but the men asked for waltzes and popular songs. Then Marco would pick up his accordion and soon the violin would be caught up in the easy rhythm of current hits. In this way the evenings passed pleasantly enough. As he packed his suitcase Denis thought that maybe here he had lived the best moments of his life.

On the next bed the student, stiff as a corpse, lay dreaming with his eyes open. He was shaken from time to time by fits of coughing.

"What the hell are they up to, those two? Can't someone put some more coal on the fire?"

Coal—almost incombustible coke that they scrounged from ashes and dross iron on the street.

"Let me have your covers," said the student.

The poor boy would not be at La Hetraie very long, for here they had no facilities to treat him. In a few days he would have to go to a hospital and probably then on to a sanatorium.

Fifteen days before Denis, returning in the truck from a junk delivery, had found the boy in Neuilly, huddled in a doorway. The student had confided:

"You're lucky. You have a roof. I sleep in the woods. You have covers. I only have my clothes. You have a stove. I only have the road. I walk at night so I won't get sick. I'm alone. You are together with friends."

And now how could the boy complain after all that? How could he protest when wind whistled through the cracked boards of the old car that stood precariously on wooden beams instead of wheels and whose badly joined windowpanes rattled with the wind? A dead branch tapped on the roof with deliberate strokes. Little puddles were forming on the floor under the camp beds and mattresses. The smell of tobacco, wet wool, leather, mud, and unwashed humanity constricted their throats, and the men had the feeling that the old car was sinking lower and lower into the mud.

Denis looked at the miserable shelter and his heart sank. What would become of these Companions he was abandoning in this desert of disaster? His faith was his only authority. Believers or not, they recognized it as such. But he had converted no one. He had not tried. They had always respected him as a future priest, a reflection of their devoted affection for the Father. In a way they felt Denis was the Father's "deputy" and delegate. No, he had converted no one. But who knows? In one of the loads of junk old man Tardi had discovered a crucifix which he mended, cleaned, and hung on the wall of the wagon. He had said that it looked right up there, that when the Father came to see them he would be pleased. And no one had objected. So the crucifix on the wall awaited the Father's visit. And Denis silently entrusted to Abbé Pierre the lost souls he was leaving behind.

"Just mark my word: they'll spend the night getting drunk in the village," said the student.

It could well be. They had planned to celebrate Denis's departure all together here in the old railroad car, but once at the pub the men had doubtless started drinking and forgotten the hour. They would probably appear at dawn after Denis had left. The Foreign Legion veteran couldn't drink, anyway. Alcohol always brought on a fit of tropical fever and made him almost unmanageable. But suddenly voices, footsteps; the comrades entered cursing and shaking off the wet snow that covered them. They placed six bottles on the table.

An hour later the bottles were empty, but old man Tardi gave in and drew two liters from the barrel—two less for tomorrow. "Seven o'clock," thought Denis. "Henri was right, the car won't come now. I'll sleep here one more night."

Around him the comrades, encouraged by the violin and the accordion, were singing "The Storks Are Back Again." Old man Tardi marked the beat with his head. The Foreign Legion veteran, more excited than the rest, was banging his glass on the table. The student had returned to his bed and was sleeping through the tumult. The song was hardly finished when Marco started another one. Kurt's violin, after skipping a few bars, chimed in with the simple tune, and the voices sang out:

"Under the bridges of Paris . . ."

Henri's voice had a mellow tone, somewhat husky; the legionnaire's was irregular and hoarse, with bursts of brutal loudness. Swaying a bit from the ceiling, the oil lamp threw hard shadows on these faces, relaxed now in vague, wondrous smiles. They had forgotten Hetraie. The magic of music threw a bridge across the winter solitude to a life that was livable, warm, and carefree. Each man's memory held its own particular secrets, but the accordion and violin spoke to all of them of summer outings, Sunday dancing, of idyllic afternoons in sunlit woods, coming home late by boat along the Seine with pretty laughing girls, of the lights in the suburbs at nightfall, of the smell of gas and flowering linden trees along the quais of the Seine. Bending over his violin, Kurt was talking to his wife and little girl who were left behind in the Soviet Zone. And Denis saw before him his hard, solitary road and all the pictures of human happiness dissolving.

He felt a great need for solitude and silence. He wanted to get out into the night. Suddenly the harmony of the evening was torn to shreds. The legionnaire had caught his shoulder and was shouting:

"Listen to this. Get this one, little priest."

And blowing his wine-laden breath into Denis's face, looking at him with bloodshot eyes, he started to sing:

"The girls of Camaret claim all to be virgins." . . .

The accordion and the violin both stopped.

"There he goes again with one of his damn-fool songs."

"Shut your big mouth," said Henri. "We had that one the other day."

The legionnaire had had too much wine and he was getting feverish and irrational.

His eyes burned with hate and his mouth was distorted in cruel rage. Denis moved not a muscle to disengage the iron clamp that was nearly breaking his shoulder. He just shook his head and, in order not to excite the sick man, said: "O.K. That's fine. Change your record."

The other shouted still louder:

"The girls of Camaret are prettier than their virtue . . ."

Kurt said in his thick accent:
"Shut up, you old idiot. Get to bed."

The legionnaire stopped short, turned slowly toward the Austrian, and narrowed his reddened eyes.

"You Hun!"

There was a dead silence.

"No," said Henri and Denis together. "Don't say that."

"O.K., O.K." He calmed down suddenly, as if he realized, in spite of his drunkenness, that he had gone too far. He sank onto a bench and took his head between his shaking hands. The accordion started to play quietly.

Kurt, white as a sheet, was putting away his violin.

"I'm going out to get some air," said Denis.

Closing the door, he lifted his face to the caress of the snow and filled his lungs with the cold and bracing air. After the smoky atmosphere of the room it tasted like the fresh water of a glacial torrent. He walked in the blizzard to bid adieu to La Hetraie. He stumbled over the grooves of the road concealed under the thin layer of snow. Half blinded, he made his way to the shed where the six cement boundary markers stood in line like so many sentinels. He touched them as he passed.

"Farewell. The men will finish the work we started."

On the left near a grove of elms stood the Richaud family's wagon. A light was burning. Denis stumbled against the picket fence that enclosed the yard. The dog lying in a box under the wagon started barking.

"Quiet, Diane," murmured Denis.

For a moment he was tempted to enter the wagon and say good-by to the family. But at this hour the children would be sleeping, and the Emmaus truck might be there any minute now. He touched the picket fence.

"Farewell."

Then he passed under the great linden tree in the middle of the lot. The bare branches whispered quietly under the snow's fingers. He touched the damp trunk of the tree.

"Farewell."

He followed the main road, haphazardly fenced by odds and ends of wood, rope, and iron pipes. It ran through the middle of the enclosure. Behind the fence stood two other wagons, the frame of an old bus, and two tents. Here and there faint lights shone gently through the snow-covered canvas that looked like pyramids of phosphorescent crystal; and voices and whispers reached him from the lives shut up in these shelters of canvas and snow.

"Farewell. You will be liberated."

The largest tent contained merchandise. There Denis had washed, sorted, and packed rags that the men had brought back from the various dumps. Some of these had been hung out to dry and were hardened by the cold.

"Farewell."

He touched the edge of the well which the Companions had cemented themselves, and the wall of the old hunting cabin where they now kept their tools and the jerry cans for the Berliet. Then he crossed the pine wood bordering the enclosure and came out on the road. He paused, leaning against the elm on which was hung the famous plan that Mastic had painted of the future developments.

Directly at him from the open plain came the snow-filled wind, making the board carrying all the hope of La Hetraie creak and whine there above his head.

Last summer this piece of land was neither country nor suburb, neither field nor forest. It had been merely a hiding place for wild animals at a spot where a little road came to an exhausted end. A family had come to Emmaus to ask for shelter. There was not room for them at Clos Fleuri; so the Father had acquired this piece of distant land.

A jobless and homeless ex-employee of the street maintenance department of Drancy, Richaud had wandered from one hotel to another with his wife and two children, paying 900 francs a night like the Vatier family. They had pushed two baby carriages full of belongings, leaving their suitcases in a railroad station cloakroom. Often they had walked all night, for the woman was afraid that the police might be taking poor people's children away to public-welfare agencies. They had slept on the ground by the banks of the Oise for three days and sold their linen, clothes, and minor belongings at the Flea Market. They finally went to a Red Cross center where they found shelter for a few days and obtained the priest's name and address.

When they started to tell their story to the Father he stopped them before they could finish.

"We will lodge you," he said.

That night they slept at La Hetraie in a tent. Next day the Father suggested they exploit the neighboring dump. Several days later a group of ragpickers arrived from Emmaus, installed themselves in the "forty-men-eight-horses" car. Other families settled around them, some in tents and others in gypsy wagons. They decided to establish a co-op and Richaud was made responsible. Through selling at the Flea Market and to the half wholesalers their co-op would be self-supporting. They would start building in the spring.

The development plan that Mastic had made kept up the hope and courage of these outcast men, as far removed from civilized life as the first pioneers in the United States.

Leaning against the tree trunk, Denis suffered at the idea of leaving them all. Here he had known the most precious hours of his life.

And what would he tell the head of the seminary who would certainly question him about his apprenticeship?

"There, I tried my best to live up to my ideal, by submerging myself completely into that world of real men, by living fundamentally as they did, by seeing certain injustices but not judging them, and keeping silent—that was hardest of all—and fighting desperately against injustices. I tried to love God for those who did not love Him. They always had respect for my profound faith: violent men, drunkards, desperate men, cynics, fighters, they taught me to understand the innocence of the poor, the solidarity of the unfortunate. (Only two days ago they made a spontaneous collection of oranges for one of the men who was in the hospital.) And my disappointments, too, I placed in the hands of Christ. I penetrated into the human mass like a grain of wheat that falls in mother earth. I came up more alive than before. I have discovered the meaning of prayer, which is an action, which is a *necessity* if one is to live in action."

The snow closed his eyes, made him short of breath, slid down his collar. And he repeated, "Alive, alive . . ." The warmth and joy of this thought burst forth into the dark night, empty of people and torn by the storm.

Then he heard the noise of the truck from Emmaus.

He walked back to say a final good-by to the others. On entering the car, he saw a scene of disaster. It looked as if a tornado had struck. The table had been upset and old Tardi was trying to put it back in place. The floor was strewn with broken glass and wine and blood was everywhere. Marco was washing Henri's lip from which blood was flowing into a basin. The men were straightening the beds that had been torn apart in the fight.

"I'm fed up with that damn legionnaire," said Tardi. "You can tell the Father we don't want him here any more."

"Where is he?" said Denis.

"He went out. I don't know where to."

Denis silently picked up his suitcase. He shook hands with all the men. They seemed depressed. He gave a last glance at the crucifix and thought: "Is it all to end in defeat?"

On the threshold, old Tardi put his hand on his shoulder. Embarrassed, he murmured:

"You know what we said just now? We're going to ask the Father to send us another guy like you . . . a . . ."

Joy filled Denis's heart.

"You mean a seminarist?"

"Yes. Me, I'm no believer, as you know. But the men seem to feel you represent something beyond us all. We need just that."

"Dear Lord," thought Denis. "Could it be possible that they've felt the Holy Spirit through me?"

With bowed head he went out alone and walked toward the truck that was waiting on the road.

A figure joined him at the edge of the woods.

"*Salut*, Denis," said the legionnaire.

Denis did not answer. The now sober man walked along beside him and muttered: "If you had stayed with us, this wouldn't have happened."

Once again Denis felt a wave of joy. To be not only peaceful but to be a bringer of peace.

"Don't tell the Father," said the legionnaire. "Why worry him with this story? Tell him to take good care of himself. I'm leaving tomorrow. *Au revoir*. Here, let's shake hands."

30: *The Hard Winter*

THE FATHER spent two months in bed that winter, a winter so severe that it threatened the very existence of Emmaus.

Bad weather slowed down the work, and the teams on the building lots and the garbage dumps became disorganized through idleness. The men, imprisoned in their tents, sheds, and gypsy wagons took to drinking, quarreling, fighting. Battles ensued, and stealing, too, began again.

Once more they were short of funds. Immobilized by sickness and overwork, the Father felt that in spite of the devotion of Mademoiselle and the authority of the notary, the body of his community was beginning to fall apart.

A police call announced that one of the junk trucks, abandoned by the roadside, was on fire. The drunken men of the team were fighting in a café 300 yards away.

Another call: this time from within Emmaus. A married couple had left taking with them the stove, all the furniture, kitchen pots and pans, bed linen, clothing, and everything that had been given to them when they came two months before. They probably planned to sell it all and use the money for drink.

One night the gas reservoir at Emmaus exploded for some unknown reason. The wrecking shed caught fire, leaving twelve men without shelter. And the blue parrot hanging on the wall of the shed finally got his liberty that night. He went up in a cloud of flame.

Then, one by one, the old worn-out cars met with accidents.

Some of the men fell sick and were hospitalized. And since building had been halted, they could no longer take in any homeless families.

And Abbé Pierre, nailed to the cross of immobility, was fighting despair. But when the notary entered his small cell-like room and said: "We'll never get out of this," he answered:

"I have often heard that said, and always salvation has arrived in time."

"But how can you have such confidence?"

The Father then showed him a sailing ship of metal and wood. The men at Entrepôt had presented it to him with "their profound gratitude." They had made it in a common effort. The priest quoted the words of one of them:

" 'Father, you have no right to be reckless. If something happened to you, we could not go on living.' "

"It's true," murmured the notary. "You're all we have."

And the Father cited also the gesture of the ragpickers from the garbage dump at B.: living as an economically independent unit, they had succeeded in saving 80,000 francs during the winter, enough to pay for a ten-day vacation for each man. Now they had presented that sum to the Father. Their hard-earned francs would serve to buy a new piece of land.

"Yes, everything depends on the men who work on the dumps and the building lots. But left to themselves some of them are *incorrigibly vicious*. Why should one try to save such thankless people?"

"No," said the priest. "Not one of them is irretrievably condemned."

"Remember Casino?"

The priest bowed his head.

A few weeks later, just as the Father was getting up and around, a man freed from Pontoise prison presented himself at Emmaus.

"Who sent you to us?"

"A guy in prison, Casino. He told me, 'Go to Emmaus, and don't be the rotter that I was. Tell the Father I'm sorry.' "

And from far and near the Father received other evidence that Emmaus, crossroads of moral distress, was also a crossroads of redemption.

Emmaus was an example also, a noble deed, the significance of which was now realized not only in France, but abroad as well. He had letters from London, Brussels, Algiers, and Lebanon begging him to create similar communities in every country. But he replied:

"What can I do? You must first try it yourselves."

And by these distant messages of confidence he felt elated, but often during his long hours of insomnia he murmured:

"I am but a voice in the wilderness."

Through the walls of his cell the voice pleaded for aid. He called to other men, active, young, fervent, competent, and humane, who might take charge of the destiny of the house so that he at least could suffer in peace.

And one man, an important businessman, answered his appeal. Once he had been worth millions. Now he was coming to Emmaus to seek the true sense of life, the answer to his spiritual hunger. One evening he confided to the Father:

"These lives that we snuff out all around us, Father, these crimes that we commit unwittingly, without stopping to think, just because we are rich. You have a beautiful car, the time to loiter away an afternoon on the Champs-Elysées. You wear perfectly tailored clothes and have enough money to undertake any adventure.

". . . It was five years ago. The day was lovely. She was strolling and so was I. I approached her. Some of the girls on the Champs have that special look, that simple chic and good little bourgeois appearance. It was her first adventure. It lasted two days, and in those two days I destroyed her. With my money I destroyed her life, that of her husband, and that of her children. Her husband was a small-salaried employee. He made in one month the money I spent on her that first evening. And she discovered the world of money. In a single day her husband whom she loved became in her eyes a poor nincompoop. It was as simple as that. After this taste of luxury, she could not continue to live in two rooms, to keep house, and take care of her two children. Two years later I saw her again. She was separated from her husband. Both children had been put in a boarding school and she was a kept woman. She was sick at the thought of what she had come to, but she was incapable of turning back.

"I cannot forget this evil I have done. She had told me the name of her husband and a week ago he came here to Emmaus. We sleep in the same tent, and last night he told me his story. He has no idea that it is because of me that he is now a destitute, homeless man. I beg you, Father, send me somewhere else, to the hardest job of all, and the farthest away."

"Don't you want to continue working with him, side by side, and to try to help him find his courage again?"

"I will try."

He added: "It's not my losses that made me stop and think about myself. It's Emmaus. It's here that I've started to grasp the true meaning of life."

And this man stayed on, placing at the service of the community the experience he had gained as head of a large enterprise. It was he who helped Emmaus surmount its most difficult obstacles.

At night, unable to sleep, the priest made random notes of the thoughts that ran through his mind. These often concerned the outline of a new brotherhood of ragpicker-builders which he dreamed of founding. In groups, these men would travel throughout the world to the unfortunate suburbs of overpopulated cities—"there where God is most threatened by his children."

In the hope not only of extending Emmaus, but of establishing these future worldwide community projects, he hastily made notes of his thoughts, interrupted here and there by household accounts, rough drafts of letters, and notes of a practical order: "See to the roof at Chabon's house; study roofs made of a mixture of clay and earth. . . ."

Life is not a dream, neither is it a man-made plan. It is an acquiescence. The Lord leads us through daily events. It is for us to accept or refute.

It is not merely pulling weeds that makes the corn grow faster. One must know patience through love, and watch day by day each humble effort to know its part in the slowly mounting progress of the whole.

(Reply to the Prefecture regarding Notre-Dame; level off land at Coteau. . . .)

*Had we ourselves been placed in similar circumstances of hered-
ity, education, difficulties with work, living conditions, would we
not be just as derelict, even robbers and assassins—maybe even
more unworthy than they?*

*We take it for granted, there are no angels here. But who can
tell whether here, more than one is not on his way to becoming a
saint.*

*Man has a soul, but before preaching to him about it, see that
he has a shirt on his back and a roof over that soul. Later one can
explain to him what's inside.*

*No patronizing. It's not only important to give the unfortunates
a means to live but essential also to give them a reason to live.*

*To save oneself by work to which one has freely consented, com-
munity work which shows a result.*

The same soup for them all, believers or not.

*One of them is here because he was too red. In Madrid he
would have been shot. Another came because he was too white.
In Prague he would have been hanged. Anywhere else but here
they would have slit each other's throats consciously and willingly.
Here, faced by a family out in the cold, they say: "Father, where
are the bricks?" And in a united effort they start to build. Afterward, when the discussions begin again, they are different men
because the argument has changed in tone. They have come to the
source of the problem, hunger, thirst, a roof, the cold spell; and
they have by-passed the political issues.*

*The word of a comrade: "Here we live in the infallible. If one
is a militarist, if one is to the right or to the left, one is obliged to
admit (unless he is a complete fool) that 'in this or in that I have
erred.' But when you are building houses for mothers who are
sleeping outdoors, then you know you can't be wrong. Here all is
truth."*

"Eternal life" does not mean future life. It is life today.

*Charity in social relations. Love your neighbor as he is, that is
to say as a part of the vast whole of life. The importance of family,
professional, economic, and political structures; the presence of
Christianity in economic world structures: these are presences that
will be the decisive factor in several centuries of civilization.*

*The world is not yet complete. It is being built. The creative
effort is daily continuing. God works in our daily world. Collabo-
rate with Him. Charity is the basic law on which world construction rests.*

We are born into a world of illusions, and we are always fab-

ricating fresh ones. Disillusion is the beginning of true life. You
become a man when you emerge from illusion to enter into reality.
This is true in every circumstance, education, marriage, charity.
One has to be, if not actually deceived, then at least disillusioned
to know what love really means.

No idealism. God is not only in Heaven. He is present in the
poor man who is talking at this very moment. Christ is incarnated
in this tramp, this thief, this liar. The glory of God is incarnated
in you who read, in myself who is speaking.

Note the royal independence of the poor man who needs everyone and yet depends on no one.

The drag of time when one has to work just to earn board and
lodging. Look again for the meaning of life.

Sincerity. The value the poor man attaches to this word. An
absolute, sacred value. "This man is sincere." It is with the same
accents which these men, in their extreme misery, say these words,
that the Lord will speak of each man on the Day of Judgment: "I
was hungry and you nourished me. You were sincere." All the rest
is but a means. That is the aim.

The true monk is he who, living within his order, lives also in
the midst of the masses. It is this fast-disappearing monastic institution that our world is terribly in need of today.

Never try to acquire peace of mind by chiseling on charity.

The only community experience offered to the youth of today
is military experience. Would it not be wiser to found the nation
on some other community experience, one which would be entirely
constructive and render a genuine civic service?

It is life that must create laws and not the law which must shape
life.

Life is more an acquiescence than a choice. One may choose so
seldom. One accepts or rejects the possibilities which are offered.
The only freedom man has is to hold the sail of hope taut, or to
allow it to droop through weariness. The wind comes from beyond
us.

The only real plans are those we trace out after events have
taken place.

The masses of blasphemy which rise from our earth . . . so
rarely are they hurled at the real God, the God of hunger and
thirst, the God of love. It is against false gods, those fashioned by
egotism, hypocrisy, and thoughtlessness that these blasphemies are
hurled. It is up to us to see that these blasphemies peal forth as
cries and calls to the real God, as a hymn of glory to the true God.

Respect the unfortunate man.

Try to inspire confidence in him. Deserve it yourself.

Respect his secret, his reticence. His past does not belong to us.

Respect his religious liberty. Don't make him sing psalms in exchange for a plate of soup. This would only degrade him.

Restore to man his dignity. Herein lies the great secret. Without this not one of the ragpickers could do what he does, could live in primitive conditions in the garbage dumps. In this way God will take part in his work, and sooner or later, without outside intervention, will enter into his contrite heart.

Wrench men away from shame. Let them become sober, clean, honest, industrious, and peace-loving.

Our slogan: Freedom and Justice.

With all the money in the world you will never make men. But with real men, you can make anything, including all the money that's necessary.

Lord, we cannot go on any further. Give us reinforcements, volunteers, qualified people—and no romantics. Please, God, give us help.

31: *Noëlle's Christening*
In a Dark Corner of the Chapel

WHEN in spring the priest regained his strength, he found that Emmaus had not stopped growing. His first outing was to Clos Fleuri. Fourteen wooden and brick bungalows replaced the tents and gypsy wagons. These latter had migrated to La Hetraie, where a new lot on the hill had been acquired during the winter.

On every fenced-off lot there were flower and vegetable gardens. The young lilacs, birches, and linden trees had been brought from the forest and replanted, and the roots had taken hold firmly. The gnarled apple trees in blossom gave shade to the tin-roofed wood-and-brick houses. In the grassy enclosures there were chickens, young goats, and in the back yards were rabbit hutches. Electric current had been brought in from the main line near the gasworks; ditches and wells had been dug. Children and dogs were playing together on the garden paths or in the quiet road. Washing was hung out to dry, and from the open windows fresh with curtains came the sounds of a radio playing, a baby crying, or the voice of a young woman singing. The postman and deliverymen had now made Clos Fleuri a part of their regular beat. A village had been born.

There was, for all its poverty and hodgepodge layout, a certain beauty to the little village. It stemmed from the harmony between the simple things—a tin roof, a brick wall, a black stove,

"I know," said Marcel. "It's also Djibouti to whom we owe a vote of thanks for the house."

"Nonsense," growled the latter. "You would have built it just as well on your own."

"Not fast enough to be in time for Jeanne's arrival."

And they started reminiscing, going back over the entire Emmaus story, which found in this house one of its realizations. There were the first unemployed men received at the home; then the first building lot at La Barrière; the meeting of the Father and the Vatiers under the tarpaulin; the very beginning of Clos Fleuri, when the Father had promised to make houses, children, and flowers grow; all the difficulties and the solution brought about by ragpicking; the possibility of undertaking more building on new lots.

"I was able to help men like Djibouti, but without them I could have done nothing."

The afternoon was well advanced when Marcel uncorked the champagne and stood up to pronounce a toast.

"I drink," he said, "to the health of our friends, and I can well say our saviors: to the Father and to Djibouti."

The latter changed color and murmured something, shaking his head so strangely that Mother Vatier smiled and said to herself, "The godfather can't carry his wine." But Djibouti was not drunk. Far from it. He had all his wits about him. He remembered the old madman at Nanterre who kept repeating: "Life— this can't be it. It just can't be like this—to end up this way. Real life must be somewhere else, otherwise, so help us, we've been betrayed."

"How much has happened since then," thought Djibouti. "Real life is a little like *this*—it *is* this: to sit and hold little Noëlle asleep on my lap, to listen to the Father talking, and to be among friends."

He was falling deeper into his taciturn reverie. Against his cheek he could feel the child's curls, her regular breathing against his chest, her little fingers holding tightly onto his thumb. He did not dare move lest she awaken. He wanted to prolong the joy of feeling that young life resting against him in complete trust.

Later the Father took his leave, and all the party went out for a stroll along the river's edge. On their return Djibouti felt it was time to go. They asked him to stay and spend the evening, but he begged to be excused, kissed the children of his new family, and decided he would walk back to the Home.

Marcel said he would walk with him part of the way.

The two friends walked silently along the railroad bank. The stars were bright, the night was perfumed with all the scents of the blossoming trees and the fresh greenery.

Marcel said: "Listen, Djibouti, I want to ask your advice. I'm thinking about leaving."

"Leaving?"

"Yes, leaving Clos Fleuri."

Djibouti's heart sank. He thought: *"Alors . . . it's all lost."*

Marcel explained that in his home town, Bourganeuf, there was a farm for rent, with fields, meadows, and eight cows.

"It tempts me because I've always been a peasant. And there I'll be near my mother. I have found a buyer for our house here. I can get twice as much as what building it cost me."

"Have you discussed this with the Father?"

"Yes, and he approves. He thinks it's the best thing for me. I've never been anything but a farmer and never will be."

"Then you're doing the right thing," said Djibouti, his throat in knots.

Marcel asked him if he would agree to come north to live with them. Djibouti, confused, did not know how to answer. He would see. Marcel insisted.

"Come on, what is there to keep you?"

And now Djibouti needed to be alone to calm down the overflowing emotions the day had produced. First he must think, understand, and weigh Marcel's proposition. Above all, he must assimilate the word, that ponderous word which Marcel had used during the dinner: "Savior."

His emotions had not calmed down, his throat had not unknotted when, at the end of the avenue, he heard the bell of Emmaus ringing—the bell that called the faithful to evening prayers. Djibouti felt a strong desire to see the Father at once, to speak to him alone in confidence, to tell him finally that which he had never before had the courage to say: to acknowledge the feelings he had acquired in two and a half years and which he had suppressed.

He quickened his step.

Sunday was the day the Companions would ask for an interview with the Father. On this day, in the evening, their suffering would begin again.

Returning to Emmaus after having been out on the town, there were often five or six of them waiting for the priest. Their spirits were dulled, and their hearts overflowed with the pain which had been revived by their binge in Paris. Their own solitude, thoughts of their families and children, put them unhappily in contact with their former life. They returned in a state of depression so acute that only the Father's words of comfort could help them. This utter despair was the one thing that broke their restrained silence, made them want to talk.

"Father, may I speak to you?"

They waited for him near the porch in the shade; or they would stand around in the refectory waiting for him to finish his meal. Sometimes they would timidly seat themselves at the next table, begging for a word of encouragement, or again they might wait at the entrance to the chapel, in the shadows of the park, after evening Benediction was over.

"Father . . . if you have a minute?"

Sometimes, when the source of misery was tapped, a confidence lasted a long time. And the priest listened and often the man asked for nothing more than that. Just to be listened to and taken seriously. And some of them would admit their fall, trying to justify themselves, accusing father, mother, wife, employers, proprietors, war, society, life. The priest let each one talk, until at last, overcome by his own flow of words, the man himself would discover with painful but soothing sincerity the crux, the dark, hidden core of his misery.

"I'm a dog. It's true, I am just a poor, simple rotter. I'll never amount to anything. I'm sick of myself."

Then, refusing all pity, he would arrive at the truth, cleanse himself of the indulgence of protective lying. He would admit to pettiness or to crime, but in this very admission there was hope, for the moment he refuted his own disgusting being he gave himself another chance.

The priest would listen in silence. He remembered so many conventional confessions, heard elsewhere.

But for these real orphans who had known nothing but humiliation and met with nothing but hardship, disappointment, and failure, the priest was the only human being who had not pushed them aside, was the only one who had realized their need for affection.

There were those, too, who were tormented by religion.

Until that day Djibouti had never dared ask for an interview in order to say to Abbé Pierre:

"I know, Father, what I owe you."

One evening, last summer, he had been on the verge of taking the step. They had been alone in the shed. In the rays cast by an old arc lamp the priest was tinkering with the Renault. Djibouti was just opening his mouth to form the words: "Please, Father, listen," when a drunken companion came staggering in. He was a divorcé whose children were living with his ex-wife. He had been to see them in Paris. Now he stopped short in front of them and was stammering plaintively:

"Father, Father . . ."

The Father kept on with his work as though he had not heard. The poor devil moaned the small, weak whine of a sick animal: "Father, at least smile at me." Then, disappointed, he had moved away, repeating, "I know, I know . . ."

As the man reached the door, the priest lifted his head and called him back. The priest was smiling.

But Djibouti had not dared speak to him again that evening.

The service had already started when Djibouti slipped into the chapel that he had helped build two and a half years ago. He had never attended a service there until the baptism that morning. It was not so much a deliberate refusal on his part that kept him from participating in religious service. It had been some time, since his first weeks at Emmaus, in fact, that he had given up his grudge against the cruelty of God—God who is omnipotent and who does nothing for the poor. He had forgotten also his theories that the Church was fabricated piece by piece by exploiters. He felt that the whole confusing problem was really simple and that the solution lay before his eyes in the priest's activities. The very existence of the priest was in itself the evidence of truth. At times, when Djibouti had been tempted to answer the peal of the bell which called his comrades, he resisted out of sheer shame. He thought he was not worthy of attending Mass, that he would feel out of place and would not know how to pray. The fact that he would hear unintelligible Latin was another source of irritation to him. He knew nothing about the liturgy. So he wandered off murmuring, "Later." And two years had gone by without his having ever crossed the threshold that was so close, just at the end of the park.

"How alone he is," thought Djibouti from the farthest corner of the chapel into which he had slipped. In the faint light of the choir Mademoiselle sat in her usual place slightly apart from the others. Only five Companions were in the church: the little Dominican monk who worked in the kitchen; Raoul, the man with the tattooed medal; the new seminarist who had replaced Denis; young Dédé and Patoche, the attempted suicide who had been converted recently.

How miserable it was, this handful of privileged ones who, by their consoling presence, tried to dispel the terrible solitude of the Father. How happy he had been, thought Djibouti, when we were building this chapel two years ago. He used to say that every stone would pray and that he was afraid that one day the chapel would be too small. Alas, what did it actually represent to the majority of the Companions? A sidelight, an almost unnecessary annex; but for the priest it was the center of Emmaus, the spot where the tree took root. There in the tabernacle behind the red lamp beat the Heart which animated the community.

Remorsefully, he thought he should get closer to this light so that the Father would feel less lost in his solitude among the lonely stones that were praying with him and his five Companions.

Outside, he could hear the barking of the dogs who had been let loose in the park and the voices of the comrades who were returning slightly elated from their Paris outing.

"Good Lord, during my trials Thou hast opened my heart . . . Children of men, how long will your hearts be weighed down . . ."

The hoarse and hesitating voices of Patoche and Raoul tried to follow with the others. They stumbled over the mysterious words in the little book, they hesitated and, somewhat disconcerted, continued:

"He who is kind and gives or lends to the poor shall never be undone."

The Father rose. Aided by the seminarist, he donned the white-and-gold sacerdotal robes and mounted to the altar. Djibouti, watching, said to himself he should have started sharing in these Sunday services long ago. Standing aside, he could have initiated himself into the beautiful, pacifying, purifying, and sanctifying rites. But, just as the others, he had not dared. There again he had shown his awkwardness through timidity.

The priest took the monstrance and, having slowly turned around, presented it to the almost-empty chapel. On their knees, the five Companions bowed their heads, as if dazzled by the brilliance of the sacred vessel borne by the saintlike man and by the significance of the Host in his hands. Djibouti saw in the candle glow the ray of light which, like a human look or a lighthouse beam, passed gently over him, and in passing discovered his unworthy figure huddled in the darkest corner of the chapel. This moving light would pass through the walls and go into the night to bless the men, the animals, the stones and trees, the cars, the heap of scrap iron at Emmaus, and from there to the four corners of the horizon, to the building lots, the dump piles, all the places where the men of Emmaus suffer and work. Like the dull glow of a lantern lighting face after face in a sleepy camp, the invisible light penetrated the darkness and touched, though they were unaware of it, the Companions in the tents, in the gypsy wagons, the drunkards, those in despair, the weary, the feverish ones, and those who felt hatred and obsessions awakening, those who hated each other, and those who finally had found peace.

The ray passed again over Djibouti, whose face was covered with beads of perspiration. Suddenly he felt an incomprehensible fear. Trembling, he tried to cling closer to the brick wall. He was murmuring to give himself courage, to find the familiar object of his devotion. He called:

"Father, Father."

The priest's face was hidden behind the large golden vessel. His figure was draped in the sacerdotal garments. Only his hands were visible, and Djibouti looked at those familiar hands that held unwaveringly the sacred vessels, those long hands with the long, nervous fingers which had now become rough workmen's hands with broken nails. And the vessel having been moved, the face now appeared and the eyes of the Father came to reassure the man in the shadows. His look seemed to say: "Who is there? Who is it, hiding in the shadows? Can it be you, Djibouti?"

Djibouti, the man who talks to himself, murmured from his corner:

"Yes, Father, I have come to tell you . . . Father, let me quickly tell you this: Today someone called me 'savior.' Noëlle's father called me that. I was a useless man, a 'receiver,' and now with you I have become a benefactor. I was nothing. I had nothing, and I lived for nothing. You have made me useful, you have rendered unto me my dignity, you have shown me the meaning of life."

"Blessed be God," said the Father out loud.

"Blessed be God," repeated Djibouti's comrades.

"Blessed be His holy Name," the stones which had been cemented by the hands of the anguished man seemed to echo.

Stripped of his priest's vestments, the Father, now kneeling at the foot of the altar, said the prayer of Emmaus. It was only at the end that Djibouti, passing his hands across his face, felt his tears.

"*To entrust to the Blessed Virgin all our work,*

For all those who live in the Home,

For all our brothers in the communities and in the building lots outside,

For our brothers Joseph and Peter, who have returned to the Lord,

For all those who have lived at Emmaus and who have left to pursue a new life,

For all the families whom we have helped to find shelter—in particular for the X family whose baby is so sick.

For all those families who are still awaiting help and who are pleading for help and understanding all over the world,

For all those who are helping us with their prayers, with their friendship, with their time, and their money,

*That we may be sufficiently numerous, voluntary companions,
capable of replying to all the distressed who ask us for help.*
  For Monseigneur, our Bishop,
  Our Lady of Peace,
  Our Lady of Emmaus,
  Our Lady of the Homeless,
  Our Lady of the Poor,
  Saint Francis of Assisi."
  "*Pray for us,*" replied the Companions,
  "*For us and all those who suffer on this earth.*"

The Vatiers left for the Creuse and wrote several times to
Djibouti to come and join them there. He answered that he
would visit them in the summer, after the new building lot on
the hill had gotten underway and when the Father could spare
him from Emmaus.

32: *Djibouti's Last Words*

D JIBOUTI did not go to join the Vatiers in the Creuse.
Djibouti did not leave his work at Emmaus.

He died on a lovely June day, crushed in the wreck of the old
Renault. The brakes had given way at the bottom of a hill. This
was the first time he had been at the wheel since his accident at
Étampes. He had agreed to replace a sick comrade in order to
transport building material to the new Coteau lot.

He died serving them all—the hard way, his face disfigured,
cut by fragments of flying glass, his back broken, crushed under
the car that careened across a ditch in the middle of the empty
countryside and capsized in a wheat field. He died suffering, his
head in the young wheat, his body in the mass of twisted red-
and-black metal. And during the long moments of his solitary
agony, under the beautiful, the horrible sun, he called to the
Father and to his friends. He called to the Father for help, but
he also called to him to tell him his secret, which was summed up
in two simple words. In that last moment his poor torn mouth
murmured the words he had never dared pronounce. They escaped mixed with blood and tears: *"Thank you."*

Then peace descended upon him.

That night in the chapel, watching by the body of his old
companion, the Father thought to himself:

"For the first time he looks as if he were smiling."

A new dawn would break soon. Over at Creuse little Noëlle
would smile at life.

But, just as on other mornings, young couples pushing baby
prams and helpless men and women would climb up the hill to
the Home. The Companions would leave for the garbage dumps
and the building lots. Djibouti's passing would interrupt nothing. On that day, as on the days to come, as long as human
courage remained stronger than human misery, the mission of
Emmaus would be accomplished.